THE LAST TRAIN
TO THE
CONCENTRATION CAMP

A SMALL BOY'S MEMORIES OF THE TRAIN TO BERGEN-BELSEN

Dirk van Leenen

CIDIVALE
PUBLISHING

The Last Train to the Concentration Camp
by Dirk van Leenen

PRINTED IN THE UNITED STATES OF AMERICA

ISBN 978-0-9998658-0-4

Cover design by Image Legends, LLC.
Interior design by Aerocraft Charter Art Service
Edited by John Wincek

I dedicate this third book of my trilogy to the many retired Resistance members. Even though they often had a dificult time talking about the war, they generously shared with me many details of the stories I wanted to write. This book would not have been possible without them.

And, to the brave Allied soldiers who performed so heroically in the final liberation of the Netherlands.

DIRK VAN LEENEN

ACKNOWLEDGEMENTS

The information contained in this book was collected over many hours of research at the Rijks Institute voor Oorlogs Documentatie, and also from:

Newspapers which had been allowed by the Nazis during the war, such as *Trouw*

de Ondergrondse Pers, by L.E. Winkel

the families Brandwijk and van Rijn

Zij Komen, by Ans van der Heide-Kort

a box full of documents and newspaper clippings gathered by the deceased father of the author

Gids Tweede Wereldoorlog, by Gemeentelijke Archiefdienst Rotterdam

Burgers in Bezettingtijd, by Ds Joh. Gerritsen, Jr. and Mr. Barend de Goede

For years, I resisted writing this book. There were many memories which brought with them great pain.

But the truth needs to be told.

It took me much longer than expected to relate these stories, and I shed more than a few tears writing certain passages. When I finally finished writing the book, it brought me an enormous sense of relief. I could finally let it all go from my mind.

The special black pages in the book are my attempt to illustrate for the reader some of the intense emotions which were felt so long ago, and once again while writing. Putting these stories down onto the page seemed more difficult than remembering the awful events themselves.

To this day, I'm still amazed how ordinary people coped for five long years with the lack of everything, and the great and terrible stressses of war.

CHAPTERS

THE LAST TRAIN
TO THE
CONCENTRATION CAMP

A SMALL BOY'S MEMORIES OF THE TRAIN TO BERGEN-BELSEN

CHAPTER ONE

A Nazi Plan of Desperation

At the former police office in The Hague, Hauptsturm-fuehrer (Captain) Wuerff was beside himself. Pacing heavily up and down the office, he mumbled aloud, "I know this van Rijn is a big resistance leader. And I know he has been helping to hide the Jews. But how does he do it?" His sergeant, Wilfred Huber, stirred uncomfortably at attention. He was unsure if the question was directed at him. "If I could find someone to infiltrate their organization, someone to become his 'friend' . . . Perhaps I can find a Jewish traitor. . . ."

Turning to the sergeant, he said, "I would like you to follow this man, shadow him wherever he goes. Perhaps we can finally nail him. I've been after him for nearly three years and never had a chance to pin him down for his treasonous activities."

"I would need two trucks and two squads, for this operation," the sergeant answered. "A dozen men. I will also need three pairs of binoculars, and plenty of food, so we won't lose him in the chase. And I will need written orders giving me total freedom to go wherever van Rijn takes me."

"Yes, yes," the Captain waved dismissively. "You will have it."

The sergeant saluted smartly and turned to go.

"You must stay out of sight of this van Rijn," Wuerff warned. "He is a very cunning fellow, having avoided contact with us so far. . . . We need to catch him red-handed, . . . preferably with a bunch of Jews in one of the hiding places. . . ." The Captain seemed to drift off in thought. The sergeant stood uncertainly a moment, then quietly slipped out.

AT 396 DEIMAN STRAAT, Kees was making preparations for a trip to a farm in the province of Gelderland.

"I can't take Cornelius with me this time, because the trip will take several days. But I have to hide the counterfeit IDs for our six Jews somewhere, and they better be safe," Kees said, "or I'll be sorry. I can't hide them in my clothes, . . . or on my body. I must find a way which will be completely unusual. And a way which would take too much time to find."

Johanna, his beautiful wife, came into the room where Kees had been mumbling to himself. "What have you been muttering about the past half hour? Are you thinking out loud, or just trying to solve one of your problems without consulting me?"

Kees smiled, thinking, *That's my wife, all right. Getting straight into my train of thought.* He said aloud, "I need to hide these IDs, but I don't know where. Do you have an idea?"

Johanna thought quietly for a moment. "Put them inside the bike. The Nazis will never find them there. Just pull the handles off, and roll them up inside the tubes, "Johanna suggested. "They will never find them, not unless they take the bike apart piece by piece. But you know the soldiers would never think of that." She smiled, "We've always outsmarted these Krauts."

It was still getting dark early, with winter just fading away. Kees took a walk around the block, as he usually did before he had to go on a trip. At the end of the street, two German trucks were parked, and two soldiers were sitting in the cabin. He wondered what they were doing on the corner. He noticed more soldiers in the back of the truck. Were they planning an arrest? Or a *razzia* (police raid) for the entire block? Kees racked his brain over what had happened these past few hours. Had anyone come to their house? No, nobody had.

Kees dismissed any worries about what might happen that night; but he thought, *I'd better warn Frans as well.* He passed the truck at a brisk pace and turned to the left, instead of his usual right turn, towards Frans' house.

He failed to notice the two soldiers who quietly followed him, fifty yards behind.

"Have you seen those two German trucks around the corner, Frans?" Kees asked without greeting his colleague. "It looks like they're preparing for a *razzia*. Have you heard anything from our friendly policeman?

"There must be about eight soldiers in each truck. Sixteen Nazis on our street corner means trouble."

Frans looked sternly at Kees, and asked, "You don't have any plans for tonight, do you?"

"No not tonight, but I have an important trip tomorrow—without my son this time. It will be much too long.

"I'm going to a farm in Gelderland. There are about seventy Jews in hiding. Six of them are scheduled to transfer to Switzerland in a few days, and I'm bringing the IDs for them."

"You'd better watch out that you're not followed by those trucks," Frans warned, "or by anyone else, for that matter."

"Let's plan a little distraction right now. I will warn all our Resistance friends in the area; but you need to get home unnoticed first," Frans said. He thought for a moment. "Okay, here's my plan. We need to see if you've been followed here. When you go out the front door, turn left instead of right.

"I'll watch through the peephole to see if anyone follows you. If I see someone shadowing you, I'll run outside and yell, 'Kees, you forgot something!' You turn around, and together we come back into the house.

"Get the picture? Then we will know whether they have any plans for you."

"What about the tail?" Kees asked.

"We may pass him on the way back in; but we'll act as if we don't notice. Just keep walking and talking."

"After that, you can leave my house the old way," Frans finished, ". . . the secret way. Are we agreed?" Kees nodded.

When Kees departed, he turned left, which was the longer way back to his house. He glanced behind. Yes, there were two soldiers following him.

He increased his pace, and heard as the soldiers did, too. Frans saw them pass his house moments later. He ran outside and called out, "Kees! You forgot your bag!"

Kees stopped, then turned around, and caught a glimpse of the soldiers as they ducked into an alleyway. Frans passed them by, acting as if he hadn't seen them. He took Kees by the arm and together they walked back to Frans' house. Again, they gave no notice of the soldiers, wrapped up in their own conversation.

They both breathed a sigh of relief as they reentered Frans' house. "That was a close call," Frans remarked. "Now you know that they have something in mind for you.

"You had better abandon your plans for tomorrow and wait a few days, just to be safe. Tell Johanna to be especially careful, and keep your people silent in their hiding place."

Kees left the secret way then—through a back alley, a neighbor's backyard, and a collaborator's house.

The two soldiers who had followed Kees waited for an hour, hoping that Kees would reemerge from Frans' house. Their sergeant-in-charge walked up to talk to them from the darkness of a portico across the street.

"He is still in the house," the men reported. "He came back and saw us, so we don't know if he's coming out again."

"He has to come out again, at some point. Stay here and be ready to arrest him," the sergeant ordered.

"If he hasn't come out in an hour, go into the house and do a complete search. Arrest anyone inside. We'll be on standby, and we'll park a truck across the street further down."

When Kees arrived home an hour later, the two trucks were gone. He was deep in thought about his upcoming mission. He made plans to leave the next morning, while it was still dark outside. But first, he would take his bicycle to the ferry near the Hoorn Bridge.

It was late at night when he arrived at the bridge. The ferry man had just returned from tugging a passenger across the river on his hand-pulled ferry. Across the river was a little shack, which Kees often used as a rendezvous.

"Could you put my bike in the shack for me? I need it in the morning to get out of town." The ferry man nodded. "Can you take me over to it tomorrow at 6:00 a.m.?"

The ferry agent only nodded again. He was a man of very few words, and well understood the secrecy of the Resistance.

If they follow me in the morning, I will lose them as I cross the river, Kees thought to himself. *Then I'll just disappear into the dark.* He went back the same way he had come, the secret back-way, as they called it.

THE TWO GERMAN TRUCKS had separated. One had gone on to a roadblock on the Hoorn Bridge. The other one parked across the street from Frans' house.

The soldiers' orders were clear: in one hour, search the house and arrest anyone you find. The soldiers of the second truck parked near the bridge, and carefully checked anyone who passed through the roadblock there. They hoped in particular to find Kees van Rijn.

It was midnight when Frans heard the loud footsteps of soldiers' heavy boots. With a loud banging on his door, a soldier yelled, "Open the door! Immediately!"

Frans and his wife disappeared into the hiding place they had created in their neighbor's attic. It took them only half a minute to get up there. The one opening to the attic was quietly barricaded with a heavy piece of furniture.

The Nazis had searched Frans' house before, and ransacked it many times; but they had never found the hiding place. Frans and his wife listened as soldiers broke open the front door and rummaged through the entire house.

One of the men yelled, "Ha! I found the way to the cellar! They must be in here." Several soldiers followed him down the stairs. Shots were heard as they fired at the walls of the cellar.

Disappointed, they marched back up to the first floor. The soldiers yelled, "Wherever you are, come out! Or we'll kill you when we find you!" They stayed in the house for what seemed hours. Finally the men left, with the sergeant cursing aloud.

"*Verdampte Hollanders!* Now we have no one. What are we to report to the Captain?"

The soldiers loaded into the truck, and he growled out, "Let's go!" With a roar, the truck screeched around the corner, headed back to the roadblock at the bridge and the second truck.

The two SS sergeants met at the bridge and discussed their disappointing results. "I don't think Captain Wuerff is going to be happy with this," one sergeant said. "But there's little that we can do now. We'd better go back and get a few hours of sleep."

"Wuerff won't be in his office until 9:00 a.m. Prepare for a real dressing down then," the other sergeant sighed. "Perhaps he'll have some better ideas on how to catch our culprit."

EVERY NIGHT, the big city of The Hague went into complete black-out. It was the only measure the Nazis took to avoid attacks from Allied planes.

They all knew the war was coming to a bitter end, and soon. Some soldiers were ready to defect. Others had befriended the Dutch people, just in case they had to hide from Allied troops. Better that, than to be killed in a final fight.

Early in the morning, Kees left his house through the secret back way, out through his own backyard. He climbed the poles of a balcony to the second floor of a house—that of an old lady who always cooperated with the Resistance.

Kees had a system of signals set up with her. If he would be going through her house the next day, he flashed a carbide lantern three times. If not, he flashed it three times, twice.

The old lady would switch her balcony light off-and-on to acknowledge his coded message.

On this particular morning, he entered through her balcony door, which she had left unlocked. To his surprise, he was met by the old woman, clad in her nightgown with a cup of ersatz coffee in one hand. "Good morning, Kees," she said warmly. "I felt you could use this before going on your dangerous journey.

"Do be careful. It seems that the Nazis are getting desperate, and they're shooting at anyone without warning. You are one of the few who dares to go out on the streets during curfew."

Kees grimaced, as he sipped the steaming brew, and nodded in response. He didn't feel much like talking, not when he was under pressure like this. The idea that he was being targeted by the Nazis made him want to call off his mission for the night. He took a last sip and slipped out.

In that moment, he decided to redirect his trip, and go on to another farm—one which had nobody in hiding. That way, he could safely test whether the Nazis were still following him.

If all went well, he would attempt the present mission again in a few days, for his own safety as well as that of the Jews who were now in hiding at the Gelderland farm.

At the Brandwijk farm, they had moved all of their Jews to the Gelderland farm. The farmer had had a hunch that the farm would be targeted. He was right.

When the Nazis came that night, they were ready to burn the entire farm down, just on the chance that there were Jews somewhere in hiding. But the family had been very hospitable to the Nazis when they arrived to do their dirty work. They prepared a wonderful dinner for the entire group of soldiers, along with a generous helping of their homemade *jenever* (gin).

During the quiet dinner, the SS *obertsturmfuhrer* (lieutenant) had asked them outright, "Where are the Jews that you have in hiding? Give them up and we will spare you from burning down your farm." The soldiers had cheered at the proposal, and the mood became friendlier.

The farmer stood up and raised his glass. "You may shoot me and my wife right now, if I lie," he said. "There are no Jews on this farm, anywhere. I swear on my life there are none."

"Okay," the SS commander said, "we will do one final search. If we find any indication that you have held Jews here, we will burn the place down. Let us drink now to your innocence."

They topped the glasses off with more *jenever*. With a great "Heil Hitler!" they enthusiastically dumped the liquor down their throats. Then, the soldiers went through every space on the farm.

Afterwards, the men shook hands with the farmer. The commander even patted the farmer on the shoulder, "I am glad you were honest with me," the SS commander said.

"With the war coming to an end, I would not like to remember a burning farm with Jews running out of the flames. *Zum wohl*, Herr Brandwijk." The soldiers loaded up and left.

Kees had heard the story, and he'd told the farmer that God took care of his faithful people, and that He would follow it up with a great blessing.

They had taken huge risks, both with their farm and their lives, and they were rewarded at the end, just a few weeks away from the liberation of Holland. How lucky they had been! He always looked forward to visiting the farm, and the brave family who had hidden so many Jews over the past four years.

If the Nazis were following him, they'll have a rude awakening, Kees thought, when they discovered that his trip was just a visit to friends, with no purpose for the Resistance. Hopefully, this innocent stop would get the Nazis off his back. That way, he could safely go on with his important mission to the other farm. It was important that he deliver the valuable false IDs to those fortunate few who were leaving the country so quickly.

Riding his bicycle was a therapy for Kees, especially when he was not really on a mission. With spring approaching, the signs of new life were everywhere. The fruit trees had new buds which would burst out in an array of whites and pinks. The grass, that had not yet been eaten by cows and sheep, began to form seeds. Here and there, a buttercup dared to show its golden flowers.

A few farmers had let out their sheep, thick with wool and pregnant with new life—soon-to-be-eaten lambs, a favorite dish of the Nazi officers. The promises of a new spring and summer were in the air. Kees reflected on that, while riding his bike to see his friends at the nearby farm.

When Kees reached the farmhouse, the farmer and his wife were standing at the front door, watching him. What they also saw was a German truck systematically following Kees at a slow pace and great distance. Kees seemed entirely unaware of it.

He left the bicycle near the door, and walked over to greet his friends. Before Kees could even say hello, they pushed him quickly inside. "Kees! Do you know that you've been followed here?" the farmer Brandwijk asked. "A truck is coming up to the driveway even now!"

"Oh Lord," Mrs. Brandwijk said, "they're stopping right in front! Just say you were visiting us for my birthday."

The soldiers did not ring a doorbell or knock at the door. Instead, they burst into the house with their guns drawn, loudly demanding, *"Haende Hoch!"* (Hands up!)

"*Ausweis, bitte!*" (identity card, please) the sergeant ordered. The farmer and Kees both reached for their pockets and produced their battered IDs, worn out from four years of use. The soldiers leaned over the sergeant's shoulder to examine the IDs.

Mrs. Brandwijk excused herself and said, "I have to get mine from my purse in the other room."

A soldier followed her. "No freedom in my own house," she grumbled aloud.

The soldier asked, "*Wass sagen, sie?*" (What are you saying?)

"It will take only a minute to get my ID," she explained.

The two returned to the upper room and the soldier reported, "*Nichts los hier.*" (Nothing going on here.) Then he handed Mrs. Brandwijk's ID to the sergeant.

The farmer's wife sat down at the big kitchen table, and gestured for the soldiers to sit down too. She offered to make something to eat, which eased the tension of the moment slightly. Even so, the sergeant demanded answers from Kees. "Why are you coming to this farm?" he asked. "What is your relationship? Where is your travel permit? Where do you work?"

Kees answered each question promptly and truthfully, as he showed his 'permission-to-travel' letter.

The sergeant turned to Farmer Brandwijk, "Thank you for offering us food. However, despite your kind hospitality, we have heard that you are hiding Jews on your farm. We will need to search everything."

He gave a hand signal to his soldiers. They rose and walked out of the room, determined to find people in hiding.

While they made their search, Farmer Brandwijk explained to the sergeant, "Obersturmfuhrer Spangen has cleared our farm only a few days ago. They already did a thorough search. Even under the threat of burning our home down, we passed with flying colors. . . . My friend Kees here came for a visit to congratulate my wife on her birthday."

At that point Mrs. Brandwijk walked in with a great loaf of homemade bread and a big pot of soup that smelled delicious.

"Please Jaap, would you get some plates and bowls so we can serve these gentlemen some food." To the sergeant, she said, "I trust your men will be back shortly. How many are there?"

When the soldiers came back, they shook their heads. "There is nothing to find here, sergeant. Can we sit down and eat?"

The sergeant nodded, he seemed almost embarrassed about the amiability of the situation. When all of the soldiers had been served and began to eat, Mrs. Brandwijk said, "Just a moment, gentlemen. Let us pray for this food, and for your well-being. We pray especially for your safety in the coming days, and the imminent battle. And we ask that you be granted a safe trip back to your homeland."

Automatically, the soldiers had bowed their heads as Mrs. Brandwijk said her prayer. As they finished eating, they shook hands warmly with the couple and left in good spirits. The food, and the prayer, had turned a tense situation into a memory the German men would carry with them for years to come.

CHAPTER TWO

Hauptsturmfuhrer Wuerff's Plan

The sergeant and his soldiers reported in at the old police station on the Rijwijkse Plein, in The Hague. After their formal greeting, jumping to attention with their loudly clicking boots, the Captain saluted and dismissed the other soldiers. He told the sergeant to stay where he was.

"So, what do you have to report?" Wuerff began.

"We found nothing, sir. The farm was clean."

"Nothing?!" Wuerff was instantly ablaze with anger. "You found nothing! . . . Tell me what you saw! What about van Rijn?"

The sergeant stammered a reply while standing rigidly at attention. He told his commander all that had happened the evening before. He ended with, "This man is too clever, sir. He just disappeared. But how he did, we could not seem to find out."

During the report, the commander turned red, clearly growing even angrier. "What do you mean, 'disappeared?' Don't you know you have the authority to enter any house that . . . YOU . . . SEE . . . FIT?!" His voice grew louder with every word.

He stalked around his desk, stopped right in front of the sergeant, and shouted, "Are you able to do your job?! Or do you want me to send you to the eastern front?!" The sergeant did not answer until Wuerff had returned to his desk. He dropped down into his chair and held both hands to his head.

"Sir, may I speak?" the sergeant began.

"At ease!" the Captain roared. "Only if you are going to tell me how you will solve this situation! Your future, and your life, may depend on it."

"Yes, sir. With this suspect, sir, we need an insider. Someone to tell us about his moves and his methods. He has been eluding us for years. If we can find someone who can get close to him it will give us a chance."

The Captain interrupted the sergeant abruptly. "I'll look into it. Perhaps, we can find a Jew at the jail who is willing to turn fink to save himself. Or maybe an NSB-er, a sympathizer who is operating by himself, unknown to the Resistance.

"For now, you will continue to shadow Mr. van Rijn. Cover his house, as you did yesterday, but park out of sight. Also, you may pay a neighborly visit to the NSB man who lives across the street. I'll give you his name and house number."

"Yes, sir," the sergeant replied hopefully.

"Keep a constant eye on Mr. van Rijn's house. I want you to keep your detachment on standby, ready to move out and make arrests. Learn his schedule. I want to know when he gets home, when he goes out. Have someone follow him, and find out who else he visits. Then, in the morning of the following day, arrest him and bring him to me."

"So soon?" the sergeant asked dubiously, "And without a reason for the arrest?"

"Yes. Without probable cause you can arrest him for a hearing," Wuerff replied. "After a nice, long night of questions, we will release him. We'll keep up the pressure, and keep him off balance. Soon, he will make a mistake. Then we'll have enough information to catch him in the act."

IN THE FILING CABINET which the police used to file their criminal statistics, Wuerff had built his own very special files.

One drawer held information on every Jew that he and his soldiers had arrested over the past three-and-a-half years in The Hague. Each name was followed by the address where the arrest had taken place, and the date of capture, with the wife and children included. There were over two thousand files, which meant that they had captured a great many families.

A second drawer contained only eighty files, with names and addresses, accompanied by a series of markings.

Wuerff pulled out one particular file and took it over to his desk. After the name were three marks, a star of David, a question mark, and two letters (F & C). The letters stood for 'Friend and Collaborator'. On the lower part of the file were six addresses. He jotted the addresses down on a note pad, then summoned his driver. Minutes later, they were on their way out of the station in a green Mercedes Cabriolet.

The neighbors looked on in fear when the Mercedes stopped in front of the first address on his list.

Wuerff rang the doorbell. When he knocked on the door, it felt unlatched. To his surprise the knob turned and the door swung open. Without a word, he slipped inside.

"Mr. Haagendoorn are you here?" he yelled as he began walking through the rooms. He repeated the name several times more, but quickly understood that the house was empty. It had apparently been abandoned for some time. When he went back outside, several of the neighbors had emerged from their houses.

One of them told Wuerff that Mr. Haagendoorn had moved away some months ago, and he had not left an address. Wuerff said only, *"Dancke Schoen,"* and got back into the car. He knew that if he were to question them further they would say nothing of value. It would be a waste of time.

For the next several hours, the Captain visited every one of the addresses on his list. He found the same scenario at each of them. His next visit was to the Jewish Council.

The Jewish Council had been founded in 1938, well before the war began. Influential German Jews were persuaded to join by Hitler's henchmen, with promises that they would become the leaders of all the Jews in the country.

The Council was used by the Nazis to inform Jews of new restrictions, and to distribute the Star of David to every Jew in the country—the star to be worn at all times. The Council was efficient, organized, and had every Jewish citizen on file.

To every country, the Nazis had brought their treacherous promises, while visiting the most influential Jews. Their mission was to create a Jewish Council in every country that surrounded Germany. This way, the Jews had community leaders who could direct them on whatever was going to happen next.

Later during the war, the Nazis used the Jewish Council to dictate what the Jews must do day to day, as well as to inform them when they were to depart. The Council issued letters to the Jews that instructed them when to go to the train stations, and what they were allowed to bring with them.

The members of the Jewish Councils had been carefully deceived into doing the work of the Nazis for them. Their registration of the Jews was the primary tool the Nazis used to round up every single Jew in the country.

At long last, the councilors finally came to understand how they'd been abused. Some resigned when they learned what the Nazis had in mind. Others, in order to stay alive, had remained in place and gradually moved into the role of traitors. When the war ended, some of the traitors were arrested by the Dutch government and sentenced to jail time.

Kees had visited the Jewish Council many times, mostly to bring warnings of pending round-ups and arrests. He understood the role that they were playing and was careful not to give the Council any information on upcoming operations. He also took care not to let them know of his role in the Resistance, or they might betray Kees himself.

Often, German officers could be seen with the men of the Council. Thus, it was extremely dangerous, even foolhardy, to collaborate with the Council or its members.

Captain Wuerff entered the Council office just as if he owned the place. The managing director invited him into a private office and closed the door. Then, they shook hands almost as if they were brothers. The director, Cohen, offered a cigar and a glass of wine to Wuerff. After the usual small talk, the Captain came to the reason for his visit.

"I am looking for a man by the name of Haagendoorn. He has lived at these addresses." He showed the director his list, and continued, "I need information about Mr. Haagendoorn, a place of residence. Nothing negative. In fact, it would benefit the man greatly if I found him.

"I know he should be registered here, so would you find out where I may locate him, please?"

It was most unusual for a German officer to say 'please' when demanding information. The director noticed this and thought, *He must be desperate to find this man. Perhaps I might take some small advantage of that.*

The director answered reluctantly, "Well, I will have to go through thousands of files to find him, if he's even registered here at all. Can you give me four hours to do the research?"

"Are you sure it will take so long?" Wuerff asked suspiciously.

"Well, yes, but I can put a couple of secretaries on it. However, they do cost money," the director stalled, "and as you know, we are an organization with no benefactors."

Wuerff stood up from his chair abruptly and headed for the door. He pulled it open, then paused and said over his shoulder, "I will be back in just one hour! You had better have an address for me then."

"Yes! Yes, of course," the director retreated.

"You work for us! Do not forget that," the Captain growled menacingly. Then he left, slamming the door behind him.

CHAPTER THREE

A Humanitarian Cheat

The Captain had his driver take him to the bakery in the neighborhood where Kees van Rijn lived. Baker van Zanten had received special privileges to keep his bakery in operation, and continue to make money. He was exempt from the forced labor that every Dutchman was obliged to perform.

Jan van Zanten was also recruited at that point to become an NSB man. His wife had no idea, and Jan liked to keep it that way. Often, he was asked to do special assignments for the Nazis, almost always under the threat of losing his special privileges.

When he saw Captain Wuerff come into his store, he knew that he had another assignment coming.

To avoid creating any suspicion, Wuerff waited until all of the customers had gone. Jan walked to the back of the store and out into the backyard without saying a word. The Captain followed him through.

"I have a special humanitarian assignment for you," Wuerff began, "one that will bring you good standing with your neighbors and fellow citizens." Jan raised his eyebrows skeptically as the Nazi continued.

"I am giving you special permission to distribute free loaves of bread in the coming days. As you know, the war is coming to an end, and we, the German people, wish to make a good-will gesture. We will pay for one hundred loaves of bread to be delivered to locations where we have found, shall we say, needs among the elderly.

"Deliveries will also be made to several locations where we have confiscated food in the past. This may help the citizens to soften their opinions of us. We will give you a list of addresses where you will take this bread. In two days, you will begin making deliveries," Wuerff finished.

Then he paused, and said, "You may wish to add addresses of your own, wherever you think there is a need."

"This is an excellent idea," Jan replied. "Can I get a special written permit for this? I'll need one, just in case I'm stopped by soldiers, or at road blocks. . . . I can see suspicions being raised every time I'm stopped."

"Yes, I'll take care of it," Wuerff answered. "Just one more thing: you will report to me where you are going—and where you have gone—to deliver this bread. I wish to inform my chain of command of our acts of good will."

After Wuerff had gone, Jan went inside and told his wife of the generous plan. "This will give us a good name," he said.

"It could be good for our business after the war," she agreed.

"But they want me to make a list of where we're going to take the bread," Jan worried. "Do you have any suggestions? Perhaps the orphanage would be good."

"What about a Jewish hiding place?" his wife said. "I think Kees van Rijn could help with some of those. I'll go and speak to him right away."

When Kees returned home from his "unintended" visit to the Brandwijk farm, he told his wife about his near arrest that day.

"You'd better be very careful in the days ahead. It looks like you're being followed, and even targeted by the Nazis. Maybe you'd better avoid the trip to Gelderland."

Kees shook his head, "I can't skip that trip. There are people out there waiting to get their IDs. People who have to get out of the country soon."

The doorbell rang, and they looked at each other, alarmed. But the Nazis never rang doorbells; so who would come to pay them a visit at this hour? Johanna urged, "You get into the hiding place, Kees. I will see who it is."

Slowly and fearfully, she opened the door. She was surprised to find the baker at her doorstep. "Well hello, Jan. What brings you out to see us?"

"Is your husband at home, Johanna? I have some great news that I need to share with both of you."

"Come on in, and I'll call him. Take a seat here in the living room while I find Kees." A few minutes later, they were all discussing the baker's proposal.

"Black-market bread? In this time and day? What makes you think you can get away with that?" Kees asked. "I think the Nazis will catch you the minute you get on the road."

"It was actually suggested by Captain Wuerff, as a good-will gesture, I think to make him look good when the war is over."

"Smells kind of fishy to me," Kees remarked. "Are you sure he doesn't have any secret plans behind this?"

"I don't believe so," Jan said. "I thought you might know of some places where they can use the bread. Perhaps one of the Jewish hiding places on a farm somewhere?"

"You're right, there is a huge need for food there, especially since the Nazis confiscated all of the food from the farms. I know several places where you could bring bread, but first I need to make sure this is not some set-up by the Nazis."

The discussion ended there, as Kees stood up from the table. It was his way to show that the meeting had ended. "I will let you know tomorrow," Kees said, "but first I will find out where the need is the most urgent."

The baker walked out; though he failed to look Kees in the eyes as he said, "See you tomorrow, then."

An hour later, the doorbell rang again and Johanna opened it less carefully this time. She was shoved aside as half a dozen soldiers rushed in. The old, familiar command sounded, *"Ausweiss, bitte!"* Kees and Johanna were completely surprised when the sergeant put handcuffs onto his wrists and took Kees outside without a word.

Johanna closed the door and prayed, "Lord, I know you will protect him from evil. Please give him wisdom, and bring him back to me soon. Amen."

The truck hauled Kees and his captors straight to the old police station. They took Kees to a cell and locked him up, again without a word of explanation. Hours later, Kees was led to stand in front of Captain Wuerff.

"The reason for your arrest, Mr. van Rijn, is that you have been behaving most suspiciously. You disappear from your house for days, and show up at farms for no reason. Because of this, we have been watching," Wuerff said. "From now on, you will report to me every day in person and tell me what you're up to.

"If you do not report every day at 6:00 p.m., we will be forced to arrest you, and find a new home for you in the labor camps.

This is simply a warning, you may return home now. Good day, Mr. van Rijn."

It was 11:00 p.m. when Kees finally arrived home, well after curfew. He'd had to move carefully, and avoid any contact with the patrolling soldiers. Johanna was elated to see her husband so quickly again. "I have been praying ever since you left. What was that all about?"

"They are onto us this time. Some NSB-er has tipped them off, and I now have to report in every day at 6:00 p.m. That means I can't take any trips that last more than a day. Otherwise, they'll arrest me and send me to a labor camp."

"So, what are you going to do about the Gelderland farm tomorrow?" Johanna asked.

"Despite the threat, I have to go," Kees sighed. "The war is not going to last much longer. If I can't come back, I will stay at the farm in Gelderland until the war ends. They have no reason to arrest you, so just stay put. If they ask, tell them that you have no idea where I've gone."

Johanna swallowed hard at his plan, and nodded. She trusted her husband. After all, she prayed continually for his safety. She knew that he was making the right decisions, and saving the lives of good Jewish people in the process.

"I plan to go three days from now, just to give the Captain the satisfaction of seeing me for the next couple of days at 6 o'clock. He may grow weary of me after that."

The next morning, Kees made a visit to Frans' house. He told him about the events of the past two days—his arrest, the order to report in, and the surprise visit from the baker.

"I just wonder if there might be any connection between the three events," Kees thought aloud.

"They're onto you, Kees," Frans warned. "You'll have to be very careful, with every action you take."

"I'm going out to the Gelderland farm. This is a life or death mission; but I don't intend to come back to the city after the visit. I have no interest in going to a labor camp," Kees said, then he paused thoughtfully. "What do you think about the progress the Allied forces are making, Frans?"

Kees' friend considered the question a moment, resting his head on his hands in his usual thinking pose. "I think the Allies will be here in three weeks," he grinned. Then Frans grew serious, "But who knows how severe the fighting will be in Holland? After all, it will be the final battle here. Some of the fanatics may make it very hard on the Allies. It could be slow going.

"It might be better if you stay at the Gelderland farm. I can keep an eye on Johanna and your son for you, just in case you don't show up."

"How about the baker, Frans? What do you think I should do about him?"

"Yes, let's discuss this man for a moment. What is your opinion of him?" Frans asked, "Is he kosher? Or does he work with the Nazis?"

"Jan van Zanten has been our baker for more than ten years. I've always wondered how he was able to continue his business during the war," Kees said. "I've never heard of any NSB activity that involved him. But then, I have seen Germans in his store."

"Still, even the Nazis have to buy bread," Frans allowed.

"I suppose I have no reason not to trust him," Kees said, "although his plan does come at an odd time. And he seems to have found favor with Captain Wuerff—the very man who had me arrested yesterday. I wonder, is there a connection?"

"I think we should test our baker's sincerity," Frans said. "Why not send him with a load of bread out to the Brandwijk farm? It's already been emptied and cleared. Then, we'll see if the Nazis visit the farm after the bread is delivered."

"A brilliant idea, Frans. If the Nazis go, then we know that the bread delivery is just Nazi bait."

"We'll do it twice, Kees, to be sure that it's bait. Send him to another empty farm. Then we'll know what they're up to."

"That is yet another good reason to stay home a few more days, and do my honest duty to the Fuhrer," Kees winked. "It's a good plan." The two friends parted in a good mood. Beating the Nazis at their own game was always a favorite past time.

When Jan the Baker came to Kees the next morning, he had his box-bicycle loaded with thirty great loaves of bread.

"Can I get one of those for my own family, Jan?"

"I can't do that, Kees," the baker refused. "They might count the loaves at the next roadblock, and since it says 30 on my paperwork I could get into trouble."

"Come on, Jan. Can't you go back to your store and get an extra? After all, I'm hungry too."

Jan frowned reluctantly at Kees' plea.

"Leave the box-bike here," Kees suggested, "and run back to your shop to get me one, please. Meanwhile, I'll write down the addresses you can deliver to." The baker agreed, and a few minutes later he returned with the much desired loaf of bread. Kees thanked him profusely and gave him the two addresses.

"Good luck on your trip, Jan. Let me know how it went on your way back. Those farmers won't be expecting your wonderful surprise! Happy riding."

CHAPTER FOUR

The Greatest Art Heist

Teun Haagendoorn was a very motivated NSB-er. Before the war, he was an art-buyer for museums in several countries. He knew art extremely well—in particular that of the Dutch Renaissance. Teun was also well known by the Nazis for his vast knowledge of art.

One day, at the Rijksmuseum in Amsterdam, a Gestapo officer who admired the Dutch paintings asked him a question about their value. Unknown to him, the paintings were all exact copies of the originals that had been made just before the Germans invaded the Netherlands. With his answer, Teun made a mistake which he had seriously regretted at first—but which later made him lots of money.

The Germans, and this officer in particular, had no idea that the current exhibition paintings were all copies. Teun informed him that the pictures were not real, and that the originals had all been shipped to England just before the war began. The officer was surprised, and he asked Teun how he knew about that.

Suddenly, it occurred to Teun that he should not have told the enemy about the deception, but it was too late now. He was taken to an interrogation room at the Queen's palace where, for days, he was questioned by several officers. When the Nazis realized that they'd found a real gem in Mr. Haagendoorn, they made him a proposal he would not, and could not, refuse.

Teun had become the Nazis' specialist in appraising art, and he was taken to several countries, all under German occupation. He was asked for his appraisals of literal boxcars of fine art, all of it stolen by the Nazis from museums far less fortunate (and well-prepared) than the Dutch Rijksmuseum.

Teun Haagendoorn was a Jew; but he was so valuable to the Nazis that, in this case, that fact simply did not matter. He was always accompanied by soldiers, who never let him out of their sight. Sometimes he tried to escape his more or less captive existence—only to be caught, threatened, and returned to work. The Nazis needed Teun. In fact, they needed him so much that they offered him large sums of money, in order to secure his professional appraisals of their stolen art.

The Dutch Resistance did not know about Teun's arrangement with the Nazis. When he moved out of his first house, the Resistance simply assumed that he had been send to a concentration camp.

After moving him three times, the *moffen*, (slang for German soldiers) gave him a beautiful, spacious villa in the town of Wassenaar. They had confiscated a former ambassador's residence, which also included a fine collection of valuable paintings. Teun Haagendoorn became their curator. Now he could not escape the Nazis—a staff of six soldiers and a sergeant made certain of that—nor did he want to.

The staff officers and generals who were in charge of the art confiscations knew all about Teun Haagendoorn. Unfortunately,

Hauptsturmfuhrer Wuerff did not. In fact, he was sure that this Haagendoorn was just one more Jew on the run, trying to escape the justice of the Reich. And Wuerff was about to arrest him.

At the Jewish Council, they did not know of Haagendoorn's work in assisting the Nazis with their plunder; but when they tried to find his whereabouts, they were shocked to find an address at an expensive villa in Wassenaar. They sent a messenger out to the villa to find out what he was doing, and to make sure he would go into hiding before they supplied his address to Captain Wuerff.

Within half an hour, the messenger was back at the Council and he reported that Mr. Haagendoorn was very much alive and well—and under the protection of a German staff.

Had he joined the NSB? They decided to tell Captain Wuerff that Haagendoorn was nowhere to be found, and that they suspected he had been sent to the concentration camps.

Captain Wuerff returned to the Council an hour later just as promised, and expecting his answer. When the answer was not to his liking, the Captain became raving mad. He cursed the men of the Council out, calling them fools and incompetents unable to keep track of their own people. In a great fury, Wuerff stormed out of the Council, any hoped-for fees quite forgotten.

At his office, Wuerff summoned three sergeants together. He ordered them to take some men and visit every police precinct surrounding The Hague to search out this Haagendoorn.

Two hours later, the men had found his address in the elite town of Wassenaar. Just fifteen minutes after that, Haagendoorn himself was brought to stand in front of Wuerff's desk at the old, former police station on the Rijswijkse Plein.

Mission accomplished, Wuerff thought to himself.

What the Captain did not know was that Haagendoorn had connections of his own, even if he was only dimly aware of them. All hell broke loose when the phone rang at Wuerff's office just an hour later.

At the ambassador's villa in Wassenaar, where Haagendoorn had been picked up, the sergeant in charge of the curator's safety detail had reported instantly to his superior—the Nazi general who was responsible for the greatest art heist of the century. Teun Haagendoorn's value was so profound that the general himself summoned Captain Wuerff to his office immediately.

He answered the phone on the first ring, "Yes? Hauptsturmfuhrer Wuerff here."

"Sir, General Habsberger sends his compliments, and he asks to speak with you here, at your earliest convenience," an aide replied.

"On my way." Wuerff hung up and called for his driver. He left under the impression that he was to be commended for his hard work to locate and arrest the troublesome Resistance operatives in the city.

He was mistaken in that impression.

CHAPTER FIVE

Johanna's Heart for the Enemy

At the house in the Deimanstraat, there was always a lot of action going on. To find and cook food for up to twenty refugees was a most difficult chore. The Resistance was involved, and supplied whatever they could. Visits to farms, and secretly transporting the food, supplied the rest. It was a dangerous job. Anytime a roadblock was passed, a search took place. Anything edible could be confiscated by the equally hungry soldiers.

So, the food had to be smuggled—particularly if it was valuable food, like meat or chicken. Kees had created a perfect hiding spot, and his son Cornelius always rode on top. A specially constructed seat had a box underneath it, and Cornelius always sat atop it while Kees was searched and frisked alongside. Cornelius usually appeared as a chubby little boy, with even more food stuffed everywhere under his clothes.

Box-bicycles were backwards tricycle frames that supported large wooden boxes. The rider pedaled from the back to drive a large wooden box mounted on the front. They were commonly used to move goods around the city; but their boxes were often searched. So a clever modification was made to the boxes.

Each box had a double- and sometimes a triple-bottom, and each layer had its own purpose. The fishmongers and greengrocers would keep their waste in the top box, above a double-bottom. When soldiers opened up the top lid for inspection, they would find it full of cuttings and waste, and they closed it quickly for fear of the smell. The good, smuggled food remained undiscovered, safely hidden in the double-bottom.

The contraband food would then be carefully unpacked well inside a rented building, where nosy NSB-ers would never see the treasured food being unloaded.

Toward the end of the war, the selection of food became very limited. Often, there were only potatoes, beans, or sugar beets to be had. Sometimes, Johanna ran into unexpected bargains.

One day, a bomb had struck a grocery wholesaler's store. All of the food in the store was burned in the fire, except for a large steel container. Inside the metal box were twelve cartons of dates, of twenty pounds each. They had been heated in the fire, and the sugar had caramelized, melting them all together around the fiber of the dates.

Each box had become one single, twenty-pound, square chunk of sugared-date mass.

Johanna had been helping the wholesalers' wife to salvage anything useful, when she stumbled upon the boxes of dates. She saw their potential and made a deal. For ten guilders a box she was able to take them all. A box-bicycle was rented from a neighbor and the whole lot stored in a warehouse nearby.

Johanna had also acquired a large number of sugar beets from a farmer. They too were stored in the warehouse. The beets were grated, and after six hours of boiling, the pulp was separated from the molasses that floated atop the unappealing brew.

With these ingredients, Johanna created her famous square cookies. They were very nutritious, and they lasted forever.

The recipe was fairly simple. The beet pulp was dried and baked into thin layers. Then, the dates were mixed with the thick molasses that had come from the boiled sugar beets. This paste was spread across the beet-pulp cookies. Then they were dried in the sun, on a square yard of plywood. The resulting combination formed a large sheet cookie which was then cut into three-inch squares. Johanna made hundreds of the squares, and called them "Johanna cookies."

One day, a group of soldiers searched the house for Jews, and one of them saw Cornelius eating a 'Johanna cookie.' He asked the child if he could get a piece. Cornelius knew that they had hundreds of the cookies, and that Johanna could make many more. He asked his mother if he could give the soldiers each one of the cookies.

"Of course," Johanna replied as she passed Cornelius a large plate of them. He passed one out to each of the men. It was the nicest treat the soldiers had received in months. When they left, they thanked him abundantly.

After that initial success, Cornelius went out onto the street and began handing out the Johanna cookies to every soldier that passed by. That night, Cornelius asked Kees, "Father, can I be friends with the soldiers? They love the cookies, and they are so happy when I give them away."

It was an ideal moment for an important lesson. Kees said to his little boy, "Cornelius, we are taught to love our enemies. But being friends with them does not mean that we approve of what they do, or what they have to do. The saying 'give and you shall receive' also applies to our enemy."

Cornelius thought about his father's words for days, and then he became more energetic than ever as he handed out the sweet Johanna cookies to every passing soldier.

The end of the war was closing in, and the citizens no longer had to hide their feelings so carefully. Their emotions became more evident as the Allied liberators drew closer. Some wore their joy on their faces, while others began to openly show their hatred.

There were two different types of people in Holland then, the ones who hated the Nazi troops, and those who tolerated the occupation. The latter would enjoy their liberation in gratitude, while the former would go on hating to this day.

CHAPTER SIX

The Baker on His Mission

O n his way to the first farm, in the town of Leidschendam, Jan, the baker, was stopped at several roadblocks. Every time, the soldiers wanted to confiscate his shipment of bread. They questioned his mission, and even doubted the legality of the transit letter from Captain Wuerff. Jan was repeatedly held up for hours, while a sergeant tried to check in with the Gestapo in The Hague.

Jan grew weary of his mission. He was all but ready to give up his bread to the harassing soldiers. He kept his calm for the longest time, but when the soldiers at the third roadblock began to take some of the bread, Jan lost it.

"I demand you give me an escort back to The Hague!" he complained to the captain in charge. "There, I can get an official escort to complete my mission," .

"Very well, sir," the Captain told him. "We will escort you back to your Captain Wuerff. But if we find out that he doesn't exist, or he has not approved of your mission, you will be arrested on the spot!" For a moment, Jan blinked uncertainly at the threat, almost doubting himself.

"So, is that really what you want to risk?" the captain asked. "Or, would you rather leave us your load of bread and be safely on your way? The choice is yours."

It was a great temptation for Jan to just be done with it all and go back home.

Leaving the bread in the hands of these vultures, however, would prevent that. He couldn't go back to the city and report such a failure to Captain Wuerff. Which meant he couldn't go back to his wife. But how long would that last? The war would not go on much longer.

But Jan knew that his mission was real, and the answer was clear. Failure would mean the end of his treasured bakery permit, and a sure one-way trip for him to the labor camps.

Finally, he made his decision. He would go back the 25 miles that he had gone. Back to the city, to stay at home one night, and repeat the trip with the help of an escort from Wuerff's men.

When he returned home, the escorting soldiers ordered him to take them directly to Wuerff's office, to prove his mission was legitimate. Clearly, the soldiers still held hopes that Jan had only bluffed about his mission, and they would be able to arrest him and keep the bread for themselves.

An awkward moment came about when Jan's escorting sergeant entered Wuerff's office. He pushed the baker in before him at gunpoint. The usual greeting ritual was performed and the escorting sergeant asked his questions.

Wuerff's face and neck grew red as he listened impatiently. Then, he loudly chewed out the sergeant. "YOU are questioning MY orders? My personal orders . . . my written orders . . . as forgeries?! You have held-up a very important mission. A mission that I have sent this baker to complete!

"I will report you to your commander and have you sent to the eastern front! Give me your ID, and the name of your commanding officer, now!"

The sergeant tried to explain their actions. "We . . . we were only doing our jobs, sir! . . . Following our orders. . . ."

But Wuerff was at the height of his anger. He yelled, "You and your men get out of here—now! Or I will lock you up in solitary for a week! Without food or water!"

As the sergeant saluted and stumbled out of the office, the Captain turned to look at Jan van Zanten. "Your mission is still of the utmost importance to me," he said softly. "So here is how we will get your mission back on track. . . .

"I will assign a truck with four soldiers and a sergeant to you. They will load your box-bicycle inside the truck and you will go with them. Tell them when you are a mile away from your destination, and they will unload you. Then, you will cycle to each address that you are meant to visit.

"The men will wait for your return, then load you up again to visit the next address. Once you have completed your mission, they will return to the city . . . and you will return immediately to me. Is that understood?" The baker nodded, and Wuerff said, "Then, go."

Jan began to ask a question, "But, sir, . . ." and Wuerff began to redden again. "Please, sir, it is almost night now. I cannot go riding on my box-bicycle in the dark, not during the curfew. Perhaps it would be better if we started out again early tomorrow morning?"

Wuerff swallowed the baker's remark, and finally nodded his head. "Yes. Yes, you have a good point there. You will start again in the morning, and I will instruct the sergeant in charge to pick you up at your bakery."

"Oh, but please, sir. Don't send them to pick me up at the bakery! It will only expose me. Will you allow me to come back here for the pick up?"

The Captain sighed, "Yes, I see. You have a point there, too. Okay, 6:00 a.m. Here, on the dot."

Fifteen minutes later, Jan returned to his bakery once again, to find his surprised and very inquisitive wife waiting. He had much explaining to do, and he invented many creative lies to explain away his day.

Jan knew the end of the war was coming soon. He was more than a little worried about the possible consequences, if his fellow citizens were to find out about his traitorous activities during the occupation.

Jan sighed morosely. Perhaps the deal he'd made to keep his bakery open had not been such a good one after all.

CHAPTER SEVEN

General Habsberger's Dilemma

A t the main offices of the Nazi High Command, in the ancient government buildings called The Binnenhof, General Ernst Habsberger paced back and forth across the finely carpeted floors of his office, on the horns of a dilemma.

His department was assigned to preserve all captured artwork, sculptures, and other fine antiquities. They were ordered to pack them securely into sturdy crates, and prepare it all for shipment out of the country. Soon, it would all have a new home in the Reich.

His dilemma, on this particular day, was a possible leak concerning his secret arrangements. The chance that his plans might became known, even to his comrades, was at best frightening. At worst, it could be deadly.

A leak could mean that he would have to go underground with the project. Or, it could mean arrest, and blame for stealing the entire heist of famous Dutch art.

Not one of his fellow officers knew about his dilemma. No one knew about the importance of his project, and how it would save the lives of many of his comrades at the end of the war.

Now a minor officer, a captain by the name of Wuerff, had thrown his plans into disarray. The foolish officer had arrested his most valuable art curator, the collaborator Teun Haagendoorn, for reasons unknown.

If that man talked, it could mean the end of General Habsberger and his most secret "conservation project." The art would be lost "for the Reich" and along with it, a possible escape from the end of the war.

Their secret hiding place for a large collection of priceless paintings was compromised as well, because this Captain now knew the address. *"Wass iest der loesung?"* (What is the solution?) the General mumbled aloud, "I have no one I can confide in."

The general sat down at an antique baroque desk, confiscated from one of the former Dutch finance ministers. "What are my options?" he asked aloud. He glanced around the office, suddenly realizing there could be someone listening in. He grabbed a sheet of blank paper and thought as he wrote:

> *Options to consider:*
>
> *How to deal with Haagendoorn?*
>
> > *Dismiss him? Send him to a camp as a Jew?*
> >
> > *Keep him and force him to silence?*
>
> *What to do with Wuerff?*
>
> > *Tell him a "story" and swear him to silence?*
> >
> > *Send his soldiers to the front?*
> >
> > *Include Wuerff in the secret plan?*
> >
> > *Allow Wuerff to finish his plan, with the NSB-er?*

General Habsberger paced again, and pondered his questions for a good, long time. He leaned over his desk and scribbled some additional notes. Meanwhile, the men in the outer office, Captain Wuerff and Haagendoorn among them, sat waiting.

The General sat down at his desk again, lost in deep thought. Then he spoke softly to himself, "Okay, we keep Haagendoorn. When the shipments go out of the country, we'll need him in Brazil to take care of the art. No one can do that better."

The General got up and looked into a large oval mirror, one of the fine antiques he so admired and planned to keep for himself after the war. He confirmed his decision and nodded at his reflection. He announced, "As for Wuerff, I will let him finish his plot, let him arrest his Dutchman, and with him the last group of Jews he will betray.

"Then, I will praise him for his heroism and order him to take his group, however large it is, directly to a concentration camp . . . whichever one is still active.

"After delivery, I will order him to stay at the camp until the war ends. There he may be taken in by the Americans, and he'll never speak a word about his time here."

The General nodded to himself again, and called his aide to bring in Haagendoorn. As the rattled collaborator walked in, the general opened his arms wide and hugged him warmly. "I am so sorry that this painful situation has occurred, my friend. "You should never have been treated in this manner.

"I will instruct your security detail to call me first, before any German soldier comes to bother you, or even to ask you any questions. I thank you for your service, you are invaluable to the Reich."

After he dismissed Haagendoorn, he led him to the door, and instructed the orderly to arrange for the transport of Haagendoorn back to the villa in Wassenaar.

The General waved Wuerff into his office. The Nazi captain was obviously nervous about the situation, but the General put him at ease by saying, "Please, Captain, sit down. Let's discuss our further plan of action. What exactly did you have in mind with Haagendoorn?"

"Well," Wuerff began, "I required information from him about the locations of several Jewish hiding places. We suspect these locations are being supplied by a Resistance group under leadership of a Mr. van Rijn.

"I've tried to catch this man, using an entire platoon. He has hidden hundreds of Jews. It is high time that we punished this traitor for his wicked work against the Reich."

The General nodded in approval, which made Wuerff feel more comfortable with his situation. He hoped to finish this final heroic deed for the Reich. A long-awaited promotion to major lay in the back of his mind.

"Can you accomplish this project without the use of Herr Haagendoorn?" the General inquired.

Wuerff hesitated, then nodded. "Yes I can, sir," he said. A touch of smugness crept into his voice. "That is, provided I don't suffer from any more interference."

The general stood up stiffly from his desk. He yelled, "You dare to call my attention interference?! You! You who dares to arrest one of my best agents in this country! Captain, you are on the edge of insubordination. I could send you to the front for this! If you fail to catch this van Rijn, and his hidden Jews, within one week, you will prepare for demotion and transfer. Do I make myself clear, Hauptsturmfuehrer?"

General Habsberger strode around his desk, grabbed the young captain by his arm, and pushed him towards the door.

He yelled once more, "Go, and do your duty! And don't come back without results!"

Wuerff almost stumbled from the forceful push the General gave him. He saluted and left, and the General slammed the door behind him.

Then, Habsberger turned back toward his desk with a half smile. He brushed off his tunic, and tugged once at the hem, all neat and tidy again. "That should take care of that."

Wuerff was furious, but this time only at himself. He had let his anger get the better of him and let slip a little too much arrogance. Now, the scene with the General had cost him his pride. He resolved to do everything he could to finish his work with the greatest of speed.

When he returned to the old police station, his sergeants were waiting. They saw Wuerff enter with a look in his eye that spelled trouble, and they jumped to their feet. The men stood stiffly at attention, fully expecting yet another verbal tirade from their unhappy commander.

Wuerff quietly dismissed the two sergeants with a single, soft command, "Be back here at 5:30 a.m., with two trucks and two squads of men."

CHAPTER EIGHT

The Pigeon Egg Mystery Solved

ornelius was reflecting on the time his pigeon eggs were disappearing, and how the mystery had been solved.

It was a bright sunny day in March, when Cornelius decided to climb on the roof of the warehouse next door. He wanted to check up on the pigeon nest, to see if there were any eggs to be harvested. For months now, the nests had been empty after the mystifying disappearance of their eggs.

After a brief exchange with his father—who had declared that the eggs did not belong to Cornelius, but to anyone who found them first—Cornelius had set a trap on the advice of an old spy. He had never gone back to see him since then.

In his mother's sewing box, Cornelius found a spindle of black thread. Carefully, he stretched the thread along both sides of the roof, so that anyone climbing up would break the line. Cornelius used black thread since he assumed the thief would come only at night.

When he climbed back up onto the roof a day later, he found that the thread was indeed broken. He'd gone looking for thread on the street and found some in front of the barbershop. "A-ha!"

he cried in triumph. Was it the barber? Cornelius suspected him, but felt he did not yet have enough proof. So he decided to set a second trap.

The next day, Cornelius found a bit of chalk and pounded it into dust. He spread it over the roof, just in front of the pigeon nests. For three days, he went up onto the roof every morning, to see if there were any footprints in the chalk.

There were none, so he planned to keep looking every day. Finally, after five days he saw it. Clear footprints led to the side of the roof. When he went down to the street, he saw that the chalk footprints continued to the door of the barbershop, and there they stopped.

It was the barber.

"It must have been him!" Cornelius decided. So he pushed open the door and marched into the shop. There were no customers inside, and the barber was sitting in one of his barber chairs, lazily smoking a cigarette.

Cornelius wasted no time. "You stole my pigeon eggs!" he blurted out, "and now they won't lay eggs any more—all because you took them!"

"So? And you took all the rest of them," the barber retorted.

"No! You took them all, and that is why there are no more!" Cornelius yelled at the top of his voice. "You have to leave one egg behind, or else they stop laying!"

"Ahh! Those eggs don't belong to you!" The barber kicked Cornelius out roughly and said, "Don't bother me again!"

Back out on the street again, Cornelius began to cry. Then he stopped and made a promise to himself. "I am going to make him pay for this," he said, "and I'm going the get those pigeons back to laying eggs again."

Cornelius walked strait down the street to see the pigeon breeder, and ask him for advice. "Do you know what happened to me?" he announced when he entered the breeder's house.

"No, I don't. Not unless you tell me," the old man said with a sly smile. The pigeon breeder liked the little boy, and found it precious that he always came to visit him with questions.

"Well, the barber stole all of the eggs, and for weeks there have been no eggs at all. He took them, and now the birds won't lay anything."

"Okay, this is what you need to do," the breeder said. "Get some clay. You know, the stuff they make pots with. Make some little eggs out of the clay, just like real eggs. Let them dry really good, then paint them white.

"After that, you put one clay egg in each nest. Soon you will see new pigeon eggs appearing in the nests. You don't have to mark yours, because your clay eggs will always be heavier." The breeder smiled, "So, happy harvesting to you, very soon!"

"But what if the barber takes them all again?"

"If he does, he'll take the clay ones, and he may get very mad. He will probably never climb up on the roof again." They both laughed at that prospect.

"One more thing," Cornelius asked, "where do I go to get some clay?"

"Go to the pottery maker around the corner. Tell him that you need it for me, and he will give you some."

Cornelius laughed when he imagined how mad the barber would be when he took home some of the clay eggs.

CHAPTER NINE

The Barber Gets Picked Up

Cornelius was playing out in front of the house, when a German truck pulled up to the door of the barbershop. Two soldiers, with handguns drawn, leaped out and rushed into the shop. A minute later, they came back out with the angry barber, now in handcuffs.

"What is the meaning of this?!" He loudly protested, "I have done nothing. I am innocent!"

The barber wrestled fiercely, trying to free himself from the grip of the soldiers. One of the men clubbed the barber with the butt of his pistol, and he staggered. The soldiers pushed him into the truck. They locked the door, jumped into the cab, and the truck sped quickly away around a corner. It all happened in just a single minute. No other soldiers were anywhere in sight.

A few of the neighbors had seen what happened, and they shook their heads sadly. One man said, "Good riddance. I hope they take him away to dig trenches at the front."

"He must have offended his masters to receive such a well-earned reward," another one said. "I'm going to tell Kees, perhaps he knows what has befallen his neighbor."

Cornelius had seen it all happen, and he ran home to their front door just as the neighbor walked up to ring the bell.

The ritual inside the van Rijn house was still the same. Once the doorbell rang, Johanna went to the front door carefully. Even though there were no more Jews in their hiding place, there were now two English pilots and their aircrew. Their plane had been shot down on its way home.

Every night, great formations of bombers flew over Holland, to drop their killing loads onto the industrial cities of Germany. Many bombers were hit by flak or shot down by fighters, but not all were destroyed. Many crews were able to parachute down to relative safety in occupied Holland. Often they landed nearby, in the vicinity of The Hague.

The occupation army would frequently spot the parachutes of the descending airmen. German trucks then fanned out and criss-crossed the countryside on the hunt for Allied crews. However, the Resistance often got to them first, beating the Nazis in these dangerous games. Many crews went right into the hiding places of the brave Resistance families—hiding places that only recently were occupied by Jewish families.

The van Rijn's hiding place was still in operation, as aircrews of the Royal Air Force were cared for a few days at a time. When the time was right, the men were smuggled out of Holland and sent back to England to continue to do their dangerous jobs. A few would make the trip more than once.

When Johanna saw it was only a neighbor, she called Kees to the door. The man explained what had just happened, then asked his question. Kees shook his head sadly. "No, I don't know anything about the barber's arrest. I saw them take him, too. He may have overplayed his hand as an NSB-er."

47

"Poor guy," Johanna said, "he should have never joined up with the Nazis. Who knows what they will do with him?"

Cornelius realized that the barber would no longer be able to steal his eggs. He climbed up onto the roof and checked the nests. He found several new eggs.

CHAPTER TEN

Following the Baker's Deliveries

When the baker arrived at the old police station in the early morning, the soldiers were waiting for him. Wuerff himself went to sit in the cab with the sergeant. The baker had to sit with the soldiers in the back of the truck.

The box-bicycle, with its many loaves of bread, was handed up and placed in the middle of the truck. The baker passed his three addresses forward to the Captain. He reminded the officer to drop him off at a spot which was well out of sight of the farm. Wuerff merely nodded assent.

"It is best for our cause," the baker reassured him. "If we blow my cover, I'll be in big trouble with the Resistance. Then I will be no help to anyone."

As the truck bumped along down the road, Jan thought to himself, *It is good that it's still dark outside. If anyone saw a baker and his box-bicycle come out of a German truck, they would be suspicious indeed. The farmers would then be far too nervous to accept these gifts of mercy from me.*

Jan knew better than that, but he tried to tell himself that they were gifts anyway.

Once he was unloaded, Jan looked around to see if anyone had spotted him. He was in luck, nobody ever came out on the streets before curfew ended.

He was about a mile away from the farm. When the baker got close, about a hundred yards away from the front gate, a big Bouvier began to bark. *Good*, he thought, *that gives them time to hide their Jews.*

The barking had brought the farmer and his wife to the front door. The farmer greeted him, and said to his wife, "Look who is here, Mary. The baker is bringing us bread."

"How many loaves do you need?" the baker asked.

"That depends on how much you are going to charge me."

"Nothing," the baker replied. "This time, the Germans are on a charitable mission. They're sending me out with free bread. You may have all you need, based on how many people you have to feed." The farmer instantly understood that there was something behind this—the Germans never gave food away!

"How nice," the farmer said. "Are you sure this isn't just part of some sneaky plan of the Nazis?"

The baker ignored the man's question, and sighed, "Just tell me how many loaves, and I will be gone from here."

The farmer thought for a moment, *The baker had said it depended on "how many people we have to feed." He must mean the number of Jews we have in hiding. I think the baker will tell the Nazis, and they will then raid our farm.*

"So, how many loaves then?" the baker prodded, as he opened the big box on his bicycle.

"Okay, okay, I'm still thinking," the farmer said, growing annoyed at the man. He thought to himself, *He is so obvious. Does he really think I'd be stupid enough to admit how many people we're hiding? Idiot. Since all of our Jews are gone, perhaps I can just tease them a little.*

They're coming either way. If I say two loaves, they will think I'm lying. If I ask for twelve, they'll think I have more people.

The farmer said, "Will fifteen loaves be okay?"

Without comment, Jan unloaded the bread. The farmer's wife carried them inside, her arms full to overflowing. The baker closed the box and climbed onto his bicycle, preparing to leave.

"Where else are you taking your bread?" the farmer asked.

"One farm, about six miles from here, the De Vries. The other is in Voorschoten, the Ruigrok farm."

"Why just those and us? Who gave you these addresses?"

The baker shrugged his shoulders, then said, "It was Kees van Rijn. He gave me the addresses. He thought you could use it, and said you'd be surprised."

At the news, the farmer felt a little better about the situation. "Oh, yes. We are surprised, that's for sure. Thank you for the bread, and thank you for coming!" He waved as the baker rode down the drive.

"Kees knows we have no one in hiding," the farmer mused to his wife. "It's just the two of us. So why send the bread?"

"Why did you take so much then?" she asked.

"I thought I might play with their heads a little."

"Perhaps that is what Kees is doing as well," she said.

He nodded, "You may be right." Even so, the farmer decided to send messengers to the other two farms, to warn them of a possible "humanitarian" visit. Once the baker had pedaled out of sight, he called in two of his farmhands. In short order, they jumped on their bicycles and took off in opposite directions. Each one had a written message in the bottom of his shoe.

When the baker returned to the Nazi truck, Wuerff asked, "How many loafs did you give this farmer?"

"Fifteen, sir. They were pleased with them," Jan said curtly. It took only a minute to load the box-bicycle and the baker onto the truck, and they moved out, on their way to the next stop.

The second visit was in full daylight, so Wuerff decided to stop farther away. They pulled to a stop on a silent road deep in the woods. There, no one would see them unloading.

Jan worried, *It could be kind of odd, to see a baker and his box-bicycle emerge from the woods.* As Jan pedaled onto the main road-way, sure enough, he saw several bicyclists talking to each other and looking his way.

He decided to ease their suspicions and visit with them. He rolled to a stop. "Would you like a loaf of bread for free?"

They looked at him in surprise. But with a curious look on their faces, they all said, "Yes, please!"

"Well, I have far too many loaves with me. It's fresh, but it's not going to keep for very long. I'm on a charity mission to give bread away to people—as a kindness from the Germans."

One of the cyclists looked at him cock-eyed. "Are you serious? Germans giving away bread?"

Jan smiled, "They must be feeling guilty. You know, trying to make a good impression for when the Americans come." He handed them each a loaf of bread, then pedaled away.

"How strange. Can you believe that just happened?" one of the cyclists asked. "Let's take our bread home before the Nazis change their minds!"

At the second farm, Jan was warmly welcomed. It was almost as if they knew he was coming, because they farmer and his wife already stood waiting outside their stable door.

Without the usual pleasantries, Jan asked, "How many loaves would you like? I have plenty of them left."

"Well," said the farmer, "we do have a big family here. Could you leave us with twenty?"

"I certainly can," Jan replied. *Well, they must have lots of Jews hiding here,* he thought to himself. *Wuerff will be pleased when I tell him how many they took. And then maybe I can be done with all of this.*

As Jan pedaled away, he saw the farmer and his wife wave goodbye. He gave a little wave back, and quickly rode on. Just one more stop and his mission would be accomplished.

The truck was waiting for him in the woods. In minutes, they were loaded up again and on their way to the final address. Just ten miles further, one more visit, and this whole awkward business would be over for him. He so looked forward to going back to work at his bakery again.

On the other hand, he dreaded having to explain what he'd been doing these last few days. He knew his wife would be all over him with questions.

CHAPTER ELEVEN

Quick Action of the Resistance

E arly the next morning, the baker returned his box-bicycle to the warehouse. As he walked past the van Rijn house, Kees saw him pass by through a window.

He ran to the door and called, "Hey, Jan! What happened with all the bread that you took to the addresses I gave you last week? Come on in and tell me about it. Where they surprised?"

Jan, a little apprehensive now, reluctantly entered the house behind Kees. "Yes, they were very happy to get the bread; but some did not need as much as the others. Perhaps they no longer hide anyone. The last house took all I had."

Kees patted him on the shoulder, and said, "You're a good man, Jan. Thank you. Whenever you have more surplus, let me know and I will give you some more hiding places."

As Jan walked out the door, Kees asked him casually, "You didn't tell the Nazis where you brought it, did you?"

Jan shook his head, "No. They know nothing." He slipped quickly out the door. He didn't want any more questions. Jan felt that he'd already gone too far. The Nazi captain could go fly a kite if he wanted him to do any more of these missions.

Kees knew that the baker betrayed the Resistance. Because of this "humanitarian mission" the Jews were in great danger. He decided to take immediate action and literally ran to see his friend Leo, in the Drebbel Straat.

"We need to do something very quickly!" Kees announced as he walked into Leo's home. "Can you arrange for an ambulance to take us to three farms? They're in great danger!"

It was already late evening, and the curfew had begun two hours earlier; but a German ambulance could drive around the city without being stopped.

"We will have to dress as Germans. Kees, you will act as the doctor, and I'll be your assistant. I'll go to the airport right now, hopefully there is an ambulance available."

Leo was a man of action, and he knew stealthy ways to move through the city. It was just half an hour when he returned with the ambulance. He had given Kees a uniform, adorned with the hated swastika and a doctor's name tag, before he left. Kees was dressed and ready to jump into the cabin of the vehicle.

"Shall I put the siren on?" the driver asked.

Leo shook his head, "Not yet, but when we reach a roadblock we will. Drive fast, we have no time to lose."

When the ambulance drove over the Hoornbrug bridge, they turned on the siren. They passed a column of five trucks, with dozens of soldiers aboard. Kees remarked soberly, "I sure hope these troops aren't headed for our three farms. We better hurry to make sure we're there first. We'll park away from the farm, and one of us can walk in to deliver our warning."

Once they'd arrived at the first farm, they parked the ambulance behind a patch of tall brush. Leo ran to the farmhouse and banged on the door, which startled the farmer.

Were the Nazis back again? The farmer looked out the window of the upper room, but he saw no truck. His wife ran to the front door and opened it, to find Leo dressed as a German.

"I'm a friend of Kees," he began. "We're here to warn you! A platoon of Nazis is on the road. They may be here to visit you in the next fifteen minutes."

"They think you're still hiding Jews. So be careful, and cordial. Just let them search the place and tell them the truth."

Without further ado, Leo ran back to the ambulance. In seconds, they were on their way to the next farm. Again, they parked out of sight, and this time Kees ran to the door. The farmer knew Kees and he opened the door quickly.

"What brings you here in such a hurry, Kees?" the farmer asked, "and why on God's Earth are you wearing that uniform?"

"Good to see you, too," Kees said dryly. "I'm here to bring you a warning. The Nazis are on their way, in great force. They were tipped off by the baker who brought the free bread a couple of days ago."

"Yes, I thought that was strange," the farmer nodded, "the way the baker unloaded his bread here."

"I'm sorry," Kees said, "it was all my fault. I gave him your address. The Nazis ordered the baker to visit three farms, and donate loaves of bread. I think, to sniff out Jews. We knew that you had no one in hiding.

"Anyway, be prepared. I have to run now, so good luck. The Captain is hell-bound to make a catch. But if there is no one here, they'll leave you alone after their search."

Kees returned to the ambulance. The last farm was ten miles away. "I hope they're not going there first," Leo said. "Or we'll be in big trouble."

"The baker said that they took the biggest load of bread," Kees replied, "which probably made the Nazis think that there will be a big haul there."

"Maybe we should stick around until the soldiers come," Leo said, "just in case they create any trouble. Not that we can help, but at least we may be able to offer some comfort to the farmer and his wife afterwards."

Once again they hid the ambulance, this time in a stable just half a mile from the farmhouse. Kees and Leo both walked up to the farm and were greeted by the farmer and his wife. The couple was surprised to see them arrive on foot.

They wasted no time on cordiality. "The Nazis are on their way. At least five trucks and a lot of soldiers" Leo said. "They think you have a large group of Jews hiding here, and they'll do anything to get them onto their trucks."

"Because you took so much bread, they are convinced they'll make a big catch here," Kees explained. "But, we know the farm is empty, so they will just have to swallow their pride and leave empty handed.

"We'll be waiting until it's all over, then we'll come back and see you. Be careful, and good luck."

Leo and Kees took position in the stable, half a mile away. They pulled out a pair of binoculars, and had barely set up their watch when they saw the column of trucks arrive. "They certainly didn't waste any time," Leo remarked.

They watched as the soldiers entered the farm and fanned out across the grounds to complete their search. The notorious Captain Wuerff spoke to the farmer and his wife. The man was screaming at the old couple, and the two watchers could faintly hear him.

"We know that you have many Jews hiding here! Hand them over to us now, or we will burn down your farm, and take you with us as well!"

They saw the soldiers going in and out of the side buildings, shaking their heads as they reemerged. Eventually, the men gathered around Wuerff, who had only grown more angry.

"Burn the place down!" the Captain screamed. "Every Jew in hiding will run out, or they will burn to death."

The old couple could not believe what they just heard. The farmer started toward Wuerff, protesting, "Captain, please! No!"

Wuerff simply drew his pistol and pointed it at the man.

The farmer's wife grabbed at her husband's sleeve and pulled him back to her side, pleading with him to remain silent.

Burning down a farm was a war crime, and an act of revenge. Now, the old couple would be witnesses to that terrible crime on their own home.

Knowing that there were no Jews in hiding was a comfort to Kees and Leo; but it was a torment to watch their friends' home go up in flames. He would report this crime to the Dutch authorities in England himself, Kees vowed silently. Wuerff would be held personally accountable one day.

The poor farmer and his wife watched as their farm burned to the ground. No Jews came running out of the fire. There was no one else. Even the animals that once populated the stables had all been confiscated by the Nazis months before.

Not one of the soldiers protested to Wuerff or tried to prevent this terrible thing. Some of the men understood that he had gone too far, and that they were now involved in a war crime. But no one dared to say anything. They knew it could mean an immediate death. The pistol at Wuerff's side would guarantee it. The men had seen it all before, and they had no doubt that Wuerff would use it on his own troops.

When the soldiers left, Leo and Kees could see the looks on their faces through the binoculars. A few laughed, uncaring; but most looked simply stunned. They had little choice in the matter—in the Nazi army, *"Befehl ist befehl"* (an order is an order) which must not be disputed by the lower ranks. That didn't make it any easier to be a part of it.

Once the soldiers had gone, the two watchers left their position to go and comfort the farm couple. The woman was crying and the farmer was hysterical. "Burning down my farm! How could they be so cruel? We told them, we assured them, that there was no one inside. Now, where are we supposed to live?"

Leo put his arm around the farmer's wife and said, "Believe me, I will personally make sure that our government makes good your loss. You've been one of our biggest supporters, and have hidden so many Jews. I'll make sure they help you once this ordeal is over." She continued to sob, inconsolable.

"The Americans are almost here. For the time being, we will help you any way we can. Come with us to The Hague, and we'll keep you in a safe place. We have several homes where you can stay, and be taken care of." At that, her head lifted up and she began to dry her eyes.

"By the way," Kees asked, "where did you move that last group of Jews that you had here? There were more than forty of them, weren't there?"

"Yes," the farmer replied, as his resolve returned. "We moved them to a stable about five kilometers away. It's in the middle of a great bramble bush, unseen from any road. The stable owner is taking care of them. No Nazi has ever set foot there."

"Well done, that's very good work." Kees said. "This late in the war, the Nazis are getting desperate—as you've seen—to catch any Jews that still remain.

"Especially, this Captain Wuerff," Leo agreed. "That one is a most dedicated Nazi. He attacks his work with a zeal. He must think he'll be rewarded for his dark deeds."

"Now that we've seen what was done today, that man is destined to jail, for many years to come," Kees said. "After this war is over, we will testify about him at his war crimes trial."

"I hope he hangs," the farmer said.

"If we're lucky," Kees agreed, "and God willing."

Leo ran back to the stable where they had parked the ambulance. He returned a few moments later, driving the vehicle right up to the burning farm. The farmer was astonished to see the German ambulance coming towards him.

"What on earth is that?" he asked Kees.

"That, my friend, is our disguise. And we'll use it to beat the Nazis at their treacherous games."

CHAPTER TWELVE

The Baker Is Arrested

E very day, German army trucks visited the bakery in The Hague. Whenever the bakery was open for business, a soldier would always be at the shop. Some were there to inspect the distribution stamps of the customers. Other soldiers were there to buy just about anything that the bakery had to offer.

Throughout the day, other trucks would stop to buy bread from the baker. When the day's inventory of freshly baked bread was depleted, the door was closed, and a sign was hung out that read "*Gesloten*" (Closed). The soldier inspecting the stamps was then taken back to barracks. After that, anyone who visited the baker rang the doorbell at the rear of the building.

One evening, a soldier rang the back doorbell, long after the shop had closed. When the baker saw the soldier, he just shook his head—no, we're closed—and he otherwise ignored the door. The soldier insisted by banging on the door, demanding that it be opened. Finally, reluctantly, Jan unlocked the door.

He was almost immediately sorry that he did.

In seconds, three more soldiers pushed inside while the first one slammed the door behind them. "What is this all about?" the baker yelled. "I've done nothing wrong! I have a good relationship with Captain Wuerff!"

One of the soldiers said—in Dutch, "Jan van Zanten, you are under arrest for treason." At that, Jan's mouth fell open and his skin went pale. "We're not Germans, we are the Resistance. You're being removed from this bakery to put an end to your treasonous activities until this hellish war is over."

They handcuffed him, put tape over his mouth, and pulled a bag down over his head. The baker protested vehemently and began to struggle with all his might, but the four soldiers held him tight in their strong grips. One man opened the door, and the others pushed him outside, where they loaded Jan into a waiting German army truck.

The alley was quiet, no one had seen a thing. Their capture was completed in silence. The baker's wife had heard her husband making some noises in the back, but she'd taken no notice of it. At least, not until later, when she could not find her husband anywhere.

The truck roared as it sped off, on its way to the city of Tiel. There was a farm outside of the city that hid no Jews. Instead it held captured NSB-ers.

The NSB traitors to the Netherlands were despised by the ordinary citizens. They made the Occupation lives of the Dutch much worse, by selfishly betraying their neighbors for money or food. Most NSB-ers were motivated by greed, as they received a small fee for each piece of dirty work.

The farm outside of Tiel was very isolated and well-protected from the Nazis. Inside, there were hundreds of hidden guests who had been chained to their seats. They were kept alive with water, and thin soups made with potatoes and kale. If they were lucky, they might get a slice of homemade bread with a little lard. These men were kept alive for just one reason—to receive judgement from the Dutch courts after the war had ended.

As a group, they had protested over the lack of food, and for their "unlawful captivity." One day, the men joined together as one to make a great, loud noise; but the farm was so far out of town that no one heard a thing. They yelled themselves hoarse.

Once each week, at night, the farmer gave his time to preach to them. He tried to explain how wrong they had been for betraying their fellow citizens. A few had shown some remorse, while others cursed the farmer. But the cursing only led to a silencing strip of tape across the mouth.

It was well past midnight, when the truck with Jan arrived at a drawbridge. A warning sign for a hog pestilence was duly ignored by the driver. He knew it was untrue, a ruse which had well deterred the Nazis from crossing the bridge.

The Resistance men, in their German uniforms, unloaded their prisoner. They were all were well known to the NSB men. Whenever a new captive arrived, they would jeer and make loud accusations at the four Resistance men. They called the men traitors for wearing the German uniforms.

Jan was chained to his new home, a seat in the stable. There was very little room left inside. The stable now held three times more traitors than it used to hold cows. The poor, confiscated cows had been gone for over a year now, so the stable had gradually filled to the brim with prisoners.

Jan was briefed about the rules in his new home. "Lucky for you, Jan," the farmer told him, "the war is soon coming to an end. Then, you will be transferred to a nice, federal prison while you await your day in court. Who knows what will follow after that? I'll bring you a pillow and a straw bag to sleep on. You will be fed twice a day, perhaps not well, but you will be fed. Unlike the prisons of your "friends," there will be no beatings here, no tortures. For that you should be grateful."

When the truck with the Resistance men left for home, it was nearly 4:00 a.m. They drove for two hours without incident, and parked safely at the airport barracks. There, the Resistance maintained a secret parking lot for their "liberated" German vehicles, false ambulances, and other Resistance equipment.

The German soldiers who ran the Dutch airport never realized that they were housing a major operation of the Resistance on their own captured airfield. Such was the resourcefulness of the Dutch Resistance, always working right under the noses of the enemy.

The men changed clothes and stored their uniforms in the same secret cache, ready for their next undercover mission. There were still more traitors to be rounded up. Under the cover of the pre-dawn darkness, the men slipped away to their homes in the city.

CHAPTER THIRTEEN

Captain Wuerff Grows Desperate

A t the former police office, Captain Wuerff was gazing out a window, lost in thought as he pondered his next move. He was startled when his aide knocked at the office door. A pair of soldiers had arrived from the office of General Habsberger with orders for him.

Wuerff was directed to accompany the two men to the General's office, immediately. The Captain was somewhat alarmed at the request, and asked the soldiers why there was such urgency. "You will have to ask the General, sir. We're simply carrying out his order to escort you in."

A short time later, Captain Wuerff stood at attention in front of the General's desk. His mind raced, *What is this all about? Is it van Rijn? I still need more time!* He wondered how he could convince the General that he had been betrayed by the duplicitous baker, and that his plan to catch van Rijn had been derailed.

The General let him wait, speaking not a word as he studied his paperwork, which left Wuerff feeling ever more distressed.

Finally, General Habsberger spoke. With his head down, in a low growl, he said only, "Mr. Wuerff. . . ."

'Mister.' This was not the General's usual manner of address with his subordinates, Wuerff realized. This visit was not going to go well, he thought.

"Stand at rest, Captain," The General shuffled some papers on his desk. "I have here a complaint against you, one which is very serious," the General said calmly. He tapped the page lying before him. "With all that you have done these past two weeks, you have accomplished nothing of any benefit to the Reich."

Head still bowed, the General's voice began to rise, "On the contrary, you have tarnished the reputation of the German people by burning an entire farm to the ground—apparently, for no reason at all."

The General looked up at the Captain, and said forcefully, "Mr. Wuerff, you are a complete disgrace to the Third Reich!"

The Captain swallowed the General's words in stunned disbelief. He thought he'd always been a dutiful soldier. He answered the accusation, "But sir, we are at war! And I am charged with hunting down the Jews! Burning down a farm is sometimes the only way to root them out."

"I see. So how many Jews did you catch this time, Mr. Wuerff, after burning down this farm?"

Embarrassed, Wuerff shook his head. "Not a single one, sir. The baker cheated me. He'd informed me that Jews were hiding at three farms. I used him to deliver loaves of bread on a good-will mission, and he told me that the third farm he visited had the most Jews in hiding.

"As we searched the farm, the farmer lied, and said that there were no Jews hidden there. Even so, I was convinced that there were. So, I threatened to burn down his farm . . . to smoke out these Jews. It was unfortunate that there were none. . . .

"I simply made a poor decision, sir."

"Yes, you did," the General said thoughtfully. "A decision that comes at the expense of your reputation, that of your commander, . . . and the reputation of the Third Reich!"

The General sighed, "And so, I am forced to make an example of you, as punishment for your . . . poor decision-making.

"You will gather your men and report to the train station. There, you will board the next train for the concentration camps. One of the final trains to depart, I believe, if not the last. Poetic, is it not?"

Wuerff was stunned, and he scrambled to think of a way out of his dire predicament. *My reputation . . . finished, my career . . . over! The concentration camp? . . . Are we to serve there as camp guards? Or, as prisoners?* Wuerff couldn't believe it, and was afraid to ask for clarification. *How can I escape this awful fate?* he thought, in panic.

"Sir," he stammered, "if . . . if I may make a suggestion."

"Tell me," General Habsberger replied sardonically. "I am most interested to hear your thoughts on the matter."

Wuerff ignored the slight and spoke quickly, "I'm on the trail of a notorious Resistance leader, one who has a great number of Jews in hiding. In fact, I have over a hundred Jews already awaiting transportation! I expect to catch this Dutch traitor soon, and round up his many Jewish fugitives.

"Perhaps, I could then be put in charge of their transportation? I could deliver them for disposal myself, and make amends for my error in judgement."

Wuerff looked at the General hopefully, waiting for his decision. He thought to himself, *If I give the General what he thinks he wants, then once I am in Germany, they will forget all about me. Then, I will simply go on leave and disappear until the war is finally over.*

The General considered the Captain's proposal a moment. It couldn't have been better suited to his needs, but it was best not to let the man know that. Grudgingly, the General said, "I'm not sure that you deserve this; but you are clearly motivated to catch this man, and his Jews. I will give you another two weeks to prove your worth to the Reich.

"You will report to me here every two days at 5:00 p.m. I wish to hear about your progress. No exceptions."

"Yes, sir," Wuerff replied, "Thank you, sir."

"Remember, two weeks. No more. If you have not succeeded by then, you will find yourself on that last train to the camps." The General stood up, looked Wuerff in the eyes, and said in a low voice, "One way or another, Captain, you will make that trip."

Wuerff swallowed nervously, and remained silent, awaiting his dismissal.

"Have I made myself clear, Mr. Wuerff?"

The Captain nodded his head once, at which General Habsberger shouted out angrily, "Stand at attention!"

Wuerff clicked his heels loudly and jumped rigidly to attention, biting back a flash of anger.

The general shouted again, "Do I make myself clear? Captain Wuerff!"

With a loud, "Yes, sir!" Wuerff saluted, then turned on his heel and left. As he pulled the door closed behind him, Wuerff muttered under his breath, "Damn Nazi," completely forgetting for the moment that he was one too.

CHAPTER FOURTEEN

Kees, In Hiding Himself

A t home in the Deimanstraat, Kees had a meeting with Leo and Frans, his two closest friends, and his partners in the Resistance. The curfew was still in place, so no one was allowed on the streets. With The Hague under total black-out, they came together under cover of darkness by way of the Groenendijk's warehouse next-door.

During the last months of the war, the bombers and fighter planes overhead now flew in a direction opposite to that of the early years of the war. The Germans no longer pounded England mercilessly. Now, British bombers hammered the industrial areas of Germany by night, while the American planes crossed over during the day. Across the Rhine, factories occupied with the production of guns, bombs, and other war equipment were disappearing daily.

As the planes droned by overhead, Kees, Frans and Leo discussed the burning of the farm. "It was completely against all the rules of war," Leo said indignantly.

"What makes you think the Nazis are concerned with rules?" Frans pointed out.

Kees said, "The Captain must be held accountable for torching that farm. The fact that the fire failed to expose any Jews for him must have enraged the man, but he will stand trial for this."

"Do we have a picture of this Captain?" Frans asked.

"No, I'm afraid we don't," Kees answered, "but I know his name and his face, and the name of his superior. The Captain is Hauptsturmfuhrer Wuerff, and his boss is General Habsberger."

"How can we get pictures of these two?" Frans asked.

"Maybe we can ask the German newspaper for their photos," Leo suggested. "Who can we get to contact their photographer?"

"I think Johanna could do such a thing," Kees said, "under the guise that she's writing a story for *Trouw*. I bet the photographer will be happy to get a photo credit for an article in our paper. After all, he'll need work after the war, too."

"Good, good. We'll do it," Leo said. "Okay, now that we have a plan, we need to talk about Kees' safety. Apparently, this captain is hard on your trail, Kees. You will have to go underground . . . in your own house. If you must make a trip, you'll go with one of us. We'll use female disguises, and take any steps after dark."

CAPTAIN WUERFF had just two weeks to make his catch of the Resistance traitor Kees van Rijn; but he knew that he had to have physical proof that Kees was hiding Jews. The best proof of all was to catch van Rijn in the act.

Wuerff knew he had only suspicions, and he wondered how he could get that proof. The man visited many farms, but so far Wuerff had been unable to catch him on any farm with Jews in hiding. He racked his brain for a clever way to handle the situation; but in the end, he was left with one solution: brute force. His entire future depended upon it. Wuerff said to himself, "The only way I win this fight is with greater manpower. I think six trucks and sixty men."

Wuerff called the local army barracks and asked for their unit commander. On the first ring, Stabsfeldwebel (warrant officer) Cluekiger answered the phone himself. The man was not a favorite of the Captain's, but with the precarious position he was in, Wuerff had to get the man's cooperation.

"Captain Wuerff here, *meinem freund*, (my friend). I will need four more trucks for at least a week, with thirty-four additional troopers. Can you get them for me by tomorrow morning?"

The warrant officer curtly denied Wuerff's request, "We cannot. The high command has ordered us to cease supplying manpower or trucks to outside units, sir. The Americans are coming."

"These men are required for a very important mission. General Habsberger himself has ordered this raid," Wuerff exaggerated, "and it is most important to the Reich that we accomplish this mission."

The warrant officer sighed theatrically, "Sir, you know as well as I do that this war will come to an end very soon. Why would I stick my neck out in these final hours?"

Wuerff was shocked to hear this blunt frankness—normally, he would have had the sloucher arrested and shot. But times had changed, and he needed what this man had.

Where he might have used a sledgehammer before, now he would use a needle. Wuerff persisted gently with his request. "I think surely you can make this important exception, especially as the general has ordered it himself. You may, of course, confirm it with him if you wish. Allow me to give you the number."

71

"Uh, no. Thank you, sir. That will be unnecessary," the warrant officer replied. "I would not wish to bother the general with our more mundane duties. I will send you the men. But if anything goes wrong, the responsibility is yours, sir."

"Yes, yes. Of course."

"What time do you want them, sir?"

"Have them assembled by 6 a.m. tomorrow," Wuerff replied, "I would like to be out of town before it gets light. Thank you, warrant officer; I will not forget this favor."

Wuerff smiled as he placed the phone back in its cradle. He was elated by the small breakthrough. "I have the troops," he thought aloud. "Now I have only to catch my man, and hopefully, a good number of Jews."

When the trucks arrived the next morning, Captain Wuerff had a plan in place. He invited the sergeants into his office and laid a large map on the table. On the map, he had drawn a number of large circles, from The Hague all the way to Arnhem. At every major roadblock, there was a red x-mark. There were twelve circles and twenty x-marks.

"As you know, our roadblocks are the only places where we can easily make telephone calls. At all times, you must be aware of the nearest roadblock. There, you can leave messages for me, and for each other. Every hour, each truck will check in with the nearest roadblock for messages."

He laid a photo on the desk. "Here is the man we are looking for. His name is Kees van Rijn. He rides a bicycle and sometimes has a child seat on the back."

The Captain indicated the large circles. "These are the farms that van Rijn visits. After any visit, each farm will require a thorough search for Jews. Are there any questions?"

"What do we do when we find him?"

"Do not let him know that you've found him. Split up. One truck will follow him—discreetly, while the other does a search of the farm. Keep your distance, so he remains unaware that he is being followed.

"Flash your lights if you find any Jews hiding on the farm. At that point, the truck that follows van Rijn will drive ahead and arrest him, then return him to the farm with the Jews."

A hand-drawn map used to plan Resistance movements.

"What do we do when we bring him back to the farm?"

"Good question," the Captain replied. "Arrest every Jew and bring them, along with our man, the farmer, and his wife. Take them all to the Scheveningen Jail. I will be there, awaiting you and your big catch.

"That, however, is our end goal. First, we will have to find him. For that, you have six trucks. Go to the circles nearest the city and take up position. Examine each and every bicycler who passes by. After an hour, move on to another circle and continue your inspections. Keep going until you've found him. It may take two or three days.

"Follow the same routine every day until you've caught him. Remember, this is to be only a catch-and-release, so that we may then follow him. Our goal is to catch him red-handed at a farm hiding Jews."

"Work in teams of two," Wuerff reminded them, "and stay in communication with me, or with the other teams. Now, go to your first positions and watch all traffic. I expect results within three days. Good hunting."

Two by two, the six big trucks roared away on their missions. One pair pulled up at the first circle, the well-known Hoornbrug Bridge roadblock. No one could pass this roadblock without being searched and asked to prove their identity. There was plenty of foot traffic over the next two hours, but not one bicyclist. The men moved on to the next circle, near Rotterdam.

ON THE SAME DAY, Kees and Frans departed The Hague at 7 a.m. Their first stop would be the Hoornbrug, but they did not pass through the roadblock there. Instead, the Resistance men took a

A crossroads near the Hoornbrug Bridge.

small rowboat that was always tied up beneath the bridge. Below the bridge, it was still very dark. The men kept to the shadows and moved quietly down to the water's edge. The noises of the traffic above covered any small sounds from below.

The little boat was hidden in the thickets of cattails that grew along the shore. It was attached to a cable that ran just underneath the boat and stretched across the river. Leaning over the edge of the boat, Kees reached into the water and pulled them across by hand, while Frans held the bicycles steady. The tiny splashing noises he made went unheard. When the men reached the other side, they unloaded and quietly disappeared into the pre-dawn darkness, on their way to Rotterdam.

Kees and Frans knew where all of the roadblocks were and they were careful to avoid them. Several times, they had to hide from oncoming vehicles. It was always a Nazi truck—these days, there were few Dutch civilians with any petrol to use. Besides, the two men recognized the narrow, blacked-out headlamps of the German army vehicles.

When the men finally reached the edge of Rotterdam, they discussed how to pass through the entrance to the city. It was heavily barricaded and manned by many soldiers.

"Here's what we'll do," Frans said, taking a seat on a steel park bench. It was one of the few remaining benches—all of the wooden benches had been demolished by citizens in desperate need of firewood. "You put on your wig and women's clothing, then use your lady's ID to walk across the barricade.

"God be with you, that you will pass through unrecognized. They're expecting a man on a bicycle, not an ugly woman," Frans grinned. "I am glad that you took the child seat off the bike, it would've been a dead give away."

"No pun intended," Kees smirked. "I am confident that my disguise will get me through; but what about my bicycle?"

"After you've crossed over, I'll ride my bike and pass through. There's no one looking for me. Besides, I have all of my travel papers, and they can be verified.

"After I meet up with you, I will leave my bike in your care and I'll walk back here again. Then, I take your bicycle and cross over again. The soldiers may ask questions, but I know how to handle that."

"Frans, you're a genius. You ought to get a commendation for your devious planning. I'll go get dressed, and then we can get this show on the road."

THE TWO TRUCKS had been on guard, watching the Rotterdam roadblock for well over an hour, when a man finally approached on a bicycle. They pulled out the picture of Kees that the Captain had sent, and examined it. Then they took a long look at the oncoming man.

"I don't think it's him. He doesn't look like the picture," the sergeant said thoughtfully, "but looks have been changed before. Let's go check him out."

The driver had a better idea. "We'll let the roadblock sentries check him out for us, so we don't compromise our mission. Send me in to stand close to the guards, so I can hear what they say. If there is any indication that this is our man, I'll wave you in to join us."

"Good thinking. Do it," the sergeant replied.

The driver was in place behind the guards when the man on the bike arrived at the gate. He was surrounded by soldiers who put him up against a wall, with his legs spread, and his hands up high. They searched Frans thoroughly, then took his papers and examined them closely. *"Was ist deinem nahme?"* (What is your name?) the sergeant asked sharply.

"Frans de Ruiter, sir. It is on my *Ausweis*, and my picture too. My work commander even signed my travel document."

The sergeant nodded, then looked around at the other soldiers, as if to confirm his decision to let the man go. He returned the papers and announced, *"Niegts lose, gehen mal weiter."* (Nothing wrong here, just go on.)

The driver from Captain Wuerff's detail said, "Just a minute, please. Let me see those papers. They may be forgeries."

They stopped Frans, who was already up on his bicycle, and demanded his papers once again. Wuerff's soldier took a good, long look at them, then he shook his head. "You're right, I simply wished to be sure."

77

The driver spoke to the sentry sergeant in charge, "We are looking for this man." He passed him a copy of Kees' photo. "This is Kees van Rijn. Please inform me if he passes. We'll be waiting across the street here."

As Frans pocketed his papers, he heard what the soldiers said and realized that the Germans were still hot on Kees' trail. He gave no reaction to their words, just nodded to the sentries and pedaled away. A few minutes later, he rounded a corner and found Kees waiting safely for him there.

"You were lucky you crossed before me," Frans said to Kees. They have a picture of you now. They might have seen through your girlish good looks. So, how did they treat you?"

"Well, I played it pitiful, as if I were hurting. I showed them my crumpled papers, and they hardly even looked at them. They just waved me through, without a word."

"Good. That's very good," Frans said. "Okay, now comes the hard part. Walking back is easy, but to come again on a second bicycle? That is a bit more tricky. But I do have a plan and I hope it'll work."

"What kind of a plan?" Kees asked nervously.

"Well, it all depends on how much the guards know about what soldiers do with confiscated bicycles in the city. I have a permit from the factory, where I do my slave-labor work. It says, 'Frans de Ruiter must run errands on his bicycle for the Reich. Please, do not confiscate the bicycle. Signed, the factory commander, Carll Reiter.'"

"Incredible. How on earth did you get that, Frans?"

"I copied it from a sympathetic police man, who showed it to me. I usually keep that paper in the handle of my bicycle, but now it's in the bottom of my shoe."

78

"Wow," was all Kees could muster. "You are truly a master in the arts of deception, Frans." He shook his head, and said with a smile, "So now it's forgery. I wonder what you're going to do after the war is over."

Frans left without a word. While he was certain that his plan would work, he was still a little nervous about the possible dangers. One never knew with these late-war Nazis. They were all young and fiery. Most had only been involved in the war these last six months, having come straight from indoctrination in the Nazi's youth camps.

The sentry at the roadblock saw him coming. He called his sergeant and announced, "There's that same guy again, the one who was here just an hour ago. Only now he's without his bicycle. I wonder what the heck he's up to?"

The guards had their answer, and then some, when Frans trudged back up to the roadblock. The poor man looked positively mournful. "They took away my bicycle! They confiscated it the moment I rode into the city. But I have a special permit to keep it! Why would they do this to me? Do you know?"

The sergeant rolled his eyes—another complaining Dutchman. It was going to be one of those days. He walked away and left the guard to handle it.

"They asked to see my permit," Frans continued his complaint, "but I had to tell them it was with my other bike at home. Now I have to go all the way back and get that one, just so I can show them I had a permit to keep the first one!"

The soldier shrugged, as if to say, 'What can you do?' He waved Frans on through.

"Thank you, sirs. I will be back in an hour, and I'll show you that paper as well. Thank you."

When Frans returned an hour later, they just waved him through as if he were an old friend. They had no wish to hear the rest of his story. Frans happily waved his hellos and good-byes. How he loved to lie through his teeth and fool the Nazis at their own games.

Kees was pleased to see Frans safely return with the other bicycle. "I'm glad you're back. Thankfully, we should be able to bypass the next road block through one of our Resistance friends' backyards," Kees said. "After that, we'll have clear sailing to the Gelderland farm."

Happily, the two men climbed onto their bikes and rode away through the orchards. The trees were beginning to bloom. The promise of spring was in the air again. It made them feel hopeful. Together they would enjoy a new season, and soon a newly liberated Holland.

CHAPTER FIFTEEN

Throwing Out a Net

The Allied troops were closing in. They would soon arrive in the Netherlands, and the upcoming battles would be fierce. Many of the young, newly arrived troops had little experience in war, but some were fanatical, even so. As the German army was decimated, their determination had only grown. The young men of the Hitler Youth had been well trained.

Wuerff's platoon of six trucks had moved well past the city of Rotterdam, but still nothing real had been accomplished. They had called in to their captain several times to report that they remained unsuccessful. He was patient so far, but he would not remain so for long.

"Remember," Wuerff told them, "You have only three days. Cover every throughway where a bicycle can go. Our man is like a fox, sly and vindictive, but sooner or later he will be caught."

Their next circle on the map was in the area of Utrecht. Two trucks parked at the first entrance of the city. Two more trucks took up position at the river crossings on the Old Rijn. The last two camped on the northwest edge of the city.

The soldiers understood little of the map of the Netherlands. Particularly confusing were all of the small towns and back roads surrounding the city of Utrecht.

The six sergeants conferred with each other through field phones located at the roadblocks. "What'll we do for the night?" The sergeant-major asked the others. "We can stay in place at the roadblocks. It will be curfew in an hour, and the people will no longer be on the roads."

Another sergeant offered an idea. "This man will travel more during curfew than during the day. I suggest we take up positions along rural roads that lead to Gelderland.

"Our man will most likely take one of the roads leading out to rural areas where the farms and hiding places are. I will go to Scherpenzeel. Truck two will go to Hoevelaken, and truck three to Lunteren."

The sergeant-major agreed with the plan. He added, "We'll position there, and stay for the night. If anything happens, send one truck as reinforcements, and maintain your position with the other. Good night, *kameraden*."

KEES AND FRANS passed the city of Utrecht, using a road that followed along the Old Rijn. When it began to grow dark, the two friends decided to visit a familiar farmer just outside the town of Hoevelaken. The farmer saw them coming and wondered what brought the two Resistance men to his house. He'd not had a soul in hiding for months, but their visit was always welcome.

Kees greeted the farmer with an apology, "I'm sorry to come so late, Jaap. We're on our way to a meeting in Barneveld, at a chicken farm, of all places.

"The Nazis plan to confiscate the farmer's chickens and send the poor man to the labor camps. At the same time, they'll raid the farm for some seventy Jews still in hiding there. We need to get to that farm quickly, and move the Jews to a new hiding place. Could we rest here for the night, then get up early to finish our trip to Barneveld?"

Jaap nodded, "Of course, you can stay here. However, I may have a better idea. I have a horse and a haywagon here, all loaded up with hay. I could hide you and your bicycles in the hay, and take you there right away.

"The Nazis almost never stop a farmer at night. They know we have to move fodder to our flocks all the time. I can get you there faster and safer. How about it?"

Kees and Frans deliberated. "On these country roads, there really are no Nazis out at night."

"And the sooner we get to Barneveld," Kees said, "the more time we'll have to move the Jews out."

"I say let's do it."

"Jaap, how soon can we start?" Kees asked. "And how long will it take?"

"We can leave in five minutes, and be there in just an hour. We have to rearrange the hay bales to get you inside. The bicycles we can just lay on top."

Kees agreed, and the men began unloading several bales of hay. A small gap was created in the center of the stack, to hide the two Resistance men. They climbed inside, and Jaap put the outer bales back into place. He laid the bicycles on top, took his seat, and clucked at his horse. They were on their way.

Along the same rural road that the horse and wagon traveled, two German trucks were parked in among the pine trees. There they sat invisible to any possible passers-by. The soldiers in the beds of the trucks had settled down for the night. The sergeant and sergeant-major sat awake in the cabin, taking the first watch for any possible traffic. They hoped that a bicyclist might go by, but it was only a hope. What citizen in his right mind would be riding in the middle of the night in this darkness?

The two sergeants were whispering quietly, when they heard the soft clattering of a distant horse and wagon. "What on earth is that wagon doing out this late?" the sergeant asked.

"We'll move up alongside the road," the sergeant-major softly replied. "and hide behind some trees so we can see what's coming. Make sure the driver doesn't see us. Then we'll decide what to do about him."

They did not have to wait long to see the horse and wagon go by. It was loaded with hay, and on top lay a pair of bicycles. The sergeant wondered softly, "Why would a haywagon transport bicycles as well? What do you think, could our culprit be hidden in the hay?"

"We were told that this man is very smart," the sergeant-major said, "and that he'll use any means to do his work for the Resistance. Let's follow the haywagon to wherever it unloads, and we'll see who or what comes out of it.

"Send the second truck to find the others, and tell them to converge here. Have the men wait for further instructions once they have arrived."

Once the haywagon was about a kilometer off, the first truck quietly slipped out of its hiding place in the forest. With its head-lights off, it followed slowly at a nearly invisible distance.

It was only twelve kilometers down the road when the farmer steered his horse and wagon to the right. He turned onto a narrow dirt road which led to the chicken farm near the town of Barneveld. The town was well known for its brown chickens and their equally brown eggs. The farm had several 200-foot long chicken houses. Before the war, thousands of chickens had dutifully laid their eggs day after day.

The Nazis had soon found these huge producers of eggs, not to mention the many chickens they saw available for slaughter. During their weekly runs to the chicken farm, the Nazis had so generously helped themselves that they quickly narrowed a huge inventory down to fill less than half of all the chicken pens.

As the war ground on, visits to the farm became less frequent. The production was now just a fraction of what it had been before. Nowadays, the farmer used his eggs to breed new chicks. He hoped that, after the war ended, he could regrow his stock and resume production.

Lately, the German truck had come barely once a week. The Nazis often found that there was little or nothing to confiscate.

What the Nazis did not know, was that a huge chicken pen at the far edge of the property concealed a large basement beneath its thousands of chickens. Best of all, once the chickens had all been taken, the soldiers no longer had any reason to enter that particular chicken house.

The hidden basement could not be entered from within the building. Instead, a long tunnel from the *kelder* (cellar) beneath the farmhouse connected to the distant chicken-pen basement.

This special arrangement had been created in the first year of the war. Kees and Frans had suggested it, in case the farmer and his family ever needed a shelter from the Nazis.

With the stream of Jewish refugees from the cities, the Resistance had struggled to find enough hiding places in town for them all. As they searched for locations farther away, the farms came into play. The chicken farm in Barneveld was often home to as many as 120 Jews. Each and every day, some of them were quietly transferred to other farms, or even smuggled all the way to Switzerland.

When the haywagon arrived, it was just after midnight. The chicken farmer came running outside in his night clothes, wondering who on earth would come to visit his farm in the middle of the night.

When he saw Jaap, steering his horse and wagon close to the house, he pushed open the bedroom window and yelled, "What are you doing here so late at night? Is this really something that can't wait until morning?"

"I have some people here with me! And they bring you an important message," Jaap yelled back. "So, no! It cannot wait until morning!"

The faint echoes of the two yelling men could barely be heard by the two German sergeants. They had just parked their truck in the woods that surrounded the farm. Together, Jaap and the farmer began to unload the hay from the wagon. Then Kees and Frans jumped to the ground. The two Resistance men could be clearly seen from the vantage point of the soldiers.

The sergeant-major studied them with his binoculars, then whispered, "There's our man. We've found him. There must be a great many Jews here, for him to sneak in this way."

"Let's get out of here," the sergeant said. "No one has seen us, or has any idea that we've seen them. It's the perfect setup for a raid."

"Round up all of our trucks and the men, and let's get this place surrounded," the sergeant-major replied. "We must let no one escape. We have the men and the guns to take them all, no matter how many there are."

KEES AND FRANS entered the farmhouse and took a seat in the upper room. They were exhausted and weary after the long and dangerous trip. "That was too much excitement for one day," Kees said wearily.

Teun de Ruyter nodded agreement. The chicken farmer had lived through the war with far too much excitement for his taste as well. "It's time to make an end of this war," he said. "Thank God, the Americans are coming."

With weary smiles, they all agreed.

"But meanwhile, we must keep our Jewish guests alive and well," Kees said. "The Nazis have been intensifying their round-ups, and that's why we've come to see you in the middle of the night. Before we go any further Teun, how many people do you have in hiding today?"

"We have seventy-two in our special basement. But they are safe. It has never been compromised."

"Unfortunately," Kees said soberly, "it has been now."

"But, how is that possible?" Teun asked desperately. "They have never found anything here, or anyone!"

"Remember the baker who came to see you? He brought you a so-called charity gift of bread."

"Yes, I do. That was about two weeks ago," Teun replied. "He said I could take all that he had left. So I took about forty loaves. With so many mouths to feed, we needed it badly."

"I understand you would," Kees said. "Indeed, you must. But this baker appears to be NSB. He was sent by the Nazis to find out if you had any Jews in hiding, based on the amount of bread he left behind. Well, this NSB-er reported that three farms accepted bread, and so far, two of them have had visits from the Nazis."

"One of the farms was even burned down to the ground," Frans added.

Teun was horrified.

"That's why this is so urgent! We need to move your people out of here, quickly, before the Nazis arrive."

Matter of factly, Frans asked, "Do you know anyone who can take seventy-two people right now?"

Teun set aside his shock and thought about the question for a long moment. Then he said in a low voice, "The only place I know of is the Christian Reformed Church. We can take them there for a short while. It's a kilometer and a half from here.

"I know the pastor. I'll send my wife to wake him up and help to prepare for our people. There is a large basement under the church, and I know he will help when it comes to hiding Jewish families. But we can keep them there only be for a short time—it's just too easily found."

As a Resistance leader, Kees took command. "Send your wife now; but have her come back right away. We need to prepare the group for a walk in the next hour. There is no time for delay. Hurry!"

CHAPTER SIXTEEN

Going to Church

The Nazi trucks had assembled again in the nearby town of Barneveld. On the town square, six trucks formed a large circle. The soldiers unloaded and formed up in the center. They listened closely as the sergeant-major gave them their orders

The farmer's wife, Marianne, hurried on her way to visit the pastor, pedaling her bicycle madly. On her way, she stopped at the last chicken pen and ducked inside.

Through a hidden panel, she passed along a message, warning the people hidden below of the danger to come. Hurriedly, she told them that a group of soldiers were on their way, possibly to arrest them. They all had to be ready to move out quickly.

"I'll be back in a few minutes to let you know where we're going," Marianne said. "I may even be guiding you myself. You must get ready, quickly!"

The great group of Jews where aghast at the situation, and they asked countless questions, all at once. "How do we get out of here? What can we take with us? How far will we have to go?" Time was passing quickly, and some began to rush up and down the pen, gathering their belongings.

"You can't go out the usual way," the farmer's wife said, "Not through the farm. You'll have to create another way out of this cellar. Dig out an opening, but do it in the back. If the soldiers see you, it will be the end of us all."

A group of men grabbed shovels and began to dig at the back wall of the pen. After a few minutes of frantic work, the men had created an opening large enough to crawl through, that led into the surrounding woods. Quietly, the families began to slip out to hide beyond the tree line.

The farmer's wife rolled to a stop at the church and rang the doorbell of the vicarage. Several minutes passed with no answer, so she rang the bell again. Finally, the pastor called through the door, "Who is there, at this ungodly hour?"

"I'm sorry, pastor. It's Marianne De Ruyter. We have a real emergency, with our people in hiding. German soldiers are on the way here to arrest us all. Could you take our people in for a short time, until the threat has gone away? Please?"

The pastor opened the door, and said, "Come inside. Tell me all about it, I need more detail. How many people, and how quickly can they be here?"

"I'm going back to them now, and will bring them right away, if you agree. There are seventy-two people—families—and they are desperate for help."

"Go quickly," the pastor said. "We can help with food, beds, and other needs. Let's pray that we can keep them safe until we find a better place."

"Thank you, pastor, so very much," Marianne said, and she climbed onto her bicycle. She disappeared quickly into the dark, and within minutes she was back at the chicken pen. She found the families already gathered in the woods beyond the pen.

"Follow me, quickly and quietly," Marianne told the people. "The church will take you in, and the pastor is waiting. Stay with me through the woods until we get to the church."

It took no more than ten minutes of quick walking to get the entire group to the church. The pastor led them downstairs into a large basement, where they had beds already in place. The anxious people were greatly relieved when they saw the shelter that had so quickly been prepared for them.

Marianne quickly returned to the farm and parked her bicycle at the rear of the house. Just as she did, six trucks arrived at the front in a great cloud of dust. Soldiers leaped from the trucks and scattered to cover the entire farm. A sergeant-major demanded that the farmer bring out the Jews he had in hiding.

"But sir," Teun de Ruyter replied humbly, "we have no one here in hiding."

The sergeant-major ordered his soldiers to search the entire farm. "Go from top to bottom! Check every building and every chicken house. Dig into every possible hiding place!"

After half an hour, the soldiers began to report back in, each man shaking his head. "There is nobody here, sergeant-major. No one. We did find a large cellar underneath one of the chicken houses, and it could have held a great many people. But it was completely empty."

"A large cellar, you say?" The sergeant major looked meaningfully at Teun. "Perhaps a hiding place?"

"It is a root cellar," he replied, "we use it to store feed, for when we are busy."

The reporting sergeant continued, "There was also a large hole in the far wall. It looks like it had been dug only recently. But there was no one to be found inside or out."

"And the hole?" the sergeant-major asked Teun.

"Repairs," the farmer said softly.

The sergeant-major nodded silently as he turned and slowly paced away. "I see." He stopped pacing, turned, and said to the farmer. "And yet, a question still remains. Why did you have two bicycles on the hay wagon?"

Teun scratched his head, thinking, *That's a good question. How should I answer?*

"Where have they gone?" the sergeant-major continued. "I should like to examine them."

Teun replied carefully, "They are owned by the farmer who delivered the hay. He took them back with him. He and his farm-hands use them to ride into meadows where he cannot drive his horse and wagon."

The sergeant-major seemed satisfied with the answer, but he ordered the sergeant to load the farmer and his wife onto the trucks, and recall the men. Once they were all loaded, the trucks left the farm and drove in convoy to the village of Barneveld.

The six trucks parked neatly in the town square once again. The sergeants gathered together to plan how to turn the entire village upside down. The sergeant-major ordered his sergeants to find the local NSB man.

The usual place to find local collaborators was at the town hall. And as a rule, town clerks lived next door to the town halls. One of the sergeants strode to the door and banged on it loudly. Then, he rang the doorbell several times to wake up the entire house. It was 1:00 a.m., a time when most normal people were fast asleep. The clerk, Adrian, woke up at the noise and came to the door in his night gown. Without opening the door, he called out, "What do you want?"

The sergeant raised his voice, "Open the door, now! We need to speak with you."

Shaking more from anxiety than the chilly night air, Adrian opened the door and invited the sergeant inside.

"Please sir, I'm just the town clerk, and I have done nothing wrong. What's going on at this awful hour of the night?"

"We're looking for a group of Jews who are supposed to be hiding in this town," the sergeant said. "We need to know of any places where they could be hidden. As the town clerk, you should know the town well—and where possible hiding places could be.

"So, unless you wish to be arrested, give us the addresses and assist us with our search."

The clerk shook his head, and said with a stutter, "Th-there are no hiding places here in t-t-town, sir. Some farmers outside of town have had people in hiding, b-b-but not here in town, sir. N-n-never. I am sorry I can't help you."

The sergeant-major muttered a few swear words, then left. The frightened clerk went back to his room with shaking knees, unsure what to do. Adrian was a bachelor whose entire career had been devoted to working for the village. Was it all now to end?

When the war began, he was visited by a sergeant and a group of soldiers who asked him to provide them with the town records. Adrian had protested, saying that he could not supply them, and that it was unethical for him to give them to strangers.

The sergeant informed Adrian that he had two choices. They could arrest him, and he would spend the rest of his years in a work camp in Germany. Or, he could supply them with whatever they needed, . . . and become a member of the NSB.

Adrian thought for a moment, and weighed his options. There didn't seem to be any. He asked the men if he could join

the Nazi Party without the citizens of the town knowing anything about the role he was to play.

The soldiers assured him that he could help with their work
and still remain undercover. They also said he would be rewarded
for the information that he "voluntarily" provided.

On that promise, Adrian had agreed to cooperate. Over the
past few years, he'd provided some addresses. Other than that,
he really had not exposed himself to any danger. Neither had he
been revealed to the citizens of Barneveld.

This time, he faced a real dilemma because he knew the war
was soon to end. If he betrayed his fellow citizens now, he would
be in big trouble after the war. So, Adrian decided that he would
not assist. Neither would he tell this Nazi anything about his
position in the NSB. In fact, he planned to play an opposite role.
He would find out if there was anywhere in town where people
were in hiding; then he would visit those places and warn them
that the Germans had come.

Adrian sat down and thought about it. Where could a group
of seventy-two people hide in his town? Of course, there was the
school; but as far as he knew, the school had no basement or attic
where people could be hidden. He dismissed the idea.

There was the packing facility at the edge of town, where the
farmers brought their eggs and slaughtered chickens. They had
great big coolers out there. Could the Resistance be hiding people in those? It seemed a possibility, but if the Nazis went there,
they would find them immediately.

He thought of the local church. Adrian knew the pastor well.
He was a compassionate man, but surely he would not take the
risk of hiding a large group of Jews there. On the other hand,
the church did have a very large basement, and Adrian remem-

bered that before the war the church had even housed a small group of refugees for a short while.

Adrian decided he would visit the pastor, tell him what the Nazis had asked for, and see if the pastor could be hiding anyone. He dressed quickly, slipped out the back door of his house, and took alleys and back ways to the church. It was very late, so he was surprised when the pastor opened the door of the vicarage at the very moment Adrian knocked. Perhaps the pastor was hiding someone after all.

Adrian looked up and down the street before entering the house, to be sure there were no Germans in sight. The streets were empty, and he was relieved that no one had seen him. Upon entering the vicarage, he exclaimed, "What on earth is happening in town tonight? I've seen lots of trucks and soldiers. I even had a visit from a Gestapo man! Do you know what's going on?"

The pastor shook his head, "No, Adrian. I do not." He wasn't sure if he could trust the clerk. He'd heard rumors about him in the past, that the man might sympathize with the Nazis. He decided it was better not to reveal that he was sheltering more refugees in the church basement.

"Tell me, did the Gestapo man say what they were up to?"

"I think they are on a wild goose chase," Adrian replied, "on a tip from some traitor here in town, or somewhere."

"You know, we did have people hiding at the chicken farm," the pastor said. "But as far as I understand, they've been transferred somewhere else."

The pastor looked Adrian up and down. "But I wonder why would a Gestapo man come to visit you?"

Adrian said nothing. The pastor looked at him expectantly, waiting for an answer.

"Do you have a connection with them? It would be a grave offense if our town clerk were to side with the Nazis."

Adrian remained silent.

"Let me give you some advice," the pastor continued. "They came to visit you once, so they will be back again. Next time, they may be looking for information that you do not wish to provide."

Adrian stared at the pastor in disbelief. He thought, *Does he know that I'm in the NSB?*

"I suggest, Adrian, that you leave quickly, even immediately. If you have sided with them, they will return to take advantage of you. Is there any place that you can go?"

"You may be right," Adrian said, "I do think I should leave. I don't like all of these soldiers poking around our town. I agree they may come back to see me again."

"Good," the pastor said. "You have somewhere else then?"

"I have a sister up in Utrecht. She lives alone and works at the hospital as a nurse." Adrian nodded to himself. "If I go to her, I can stay in the house, and never have to go outside."

The minister patted Adrian on the back and led him to the door. "Be careful. God go with you."

"Thank you for your advice," Adrian gushed. "I hope everything goes well here in town. Good night."

He slipped back out the door, and hurried home. In minutes, Adrian was on his way. He packed a bag and loaded it onto his bicycle. Then he locked up his home and pedaled away into the night. He took a path that led through the woods.

Adrian thought it was better to avoid any main roads—where the military would travel.

CHAPTER SEVENTEEN

Recollections on the Pigeon Eggs

I t was a beautiful, sunny morning in mid-April of 1944, and Cornelius was pulling weeds in his little garden. The cabbage seeds had sprouted, and the spinach was already tall enough to harvest.

He looked upon his strawberry plants with great satisfaction, the blooms were already forming berries. Soon he would be able to present the first strawberries to his mother. When he looked up, he saw that the pigeons had returned, and they were flying around their nests again.

Cornelius thought back to the time the pigeon eggs had been disappearing. The old spy was visiting them then, and Cornelius asked him how to solve the problem of the missing eggs.

The man had told Cornelius to get some chalk and spread it in front of the nests on the roof. The next day, he went back to see if there were any marks in the chalk.

After several days of laying down the chalk, examining it, and finding nothing, Cornelius worried he might never solve his case. Would his nests remain empty forever? Then one morning, he'd found chalk footsteps that led directly to the neighboring barber.

The man was a traitor, a member of the NSB.

Cornelius had been warned not to talk to the man; but when he saw the footprints leading to the barbershop, he knew he had to confront him. He went inside the shop and said to the barber, "You stole my eggs, Mr. Barber. I found out, and now I know for sure. You took them!"

The barber had just laughed at him. He said, "They are not your eggs. They are the eggs of the pigeons."

Cornelius answered, "But I fed the birds that laid the eggs. There's only one way that the pigeons keep laying eggs, and you ruined it."

"I wondered why there were no more," the barber replied. "You think you can change that? Well, I'll tell you what. If you get the pigeons to lay eggs again every day, then you may keep half and I will take the other half."

"But I set it all up!" Cornelius said. "This isn't fair. You're letting me do the work, and then you take the eggs? I'm going to the police and tell them that you stole my eggs."

He had stalked out of the barbershop angrily, but the barber called out, "Wait! Let's make a better deal."

Cornelius turned around to face the barber, and said, "Okay, I'll give you one egg from every ten that I take out, and that is all. You'd better take the deal."

Without another word, he had walked out of the shop and climbed up on the roof. He did what the pigeon breeder down the street had told him to do.

"Go find yourself some clay, you can get some at the pottery shop. At home you make eggs out of the clay, in the size of the pigeon eggs, of course. When they're dry, paint them white. Then, put one in every nest.

"The pigeons don't know any better and think, because there is only one egg, they must lay a second one.

"Once they start laying, you take out the lighter one, because you know that the clay egg is heavier. That way, you can keep harvesting eggs, day by day."

The ruse worked, and the birds had begun to lay again. So Cornelius had kept his word to the barber. Every day, when he'd gathered twenty or thirty eggs, he brought two or three of them to the barber shop.

In a way, Cornelius and the barber had become like friends. He didn't exactly like the man, but he no longer hated him either. Cornelius saw him every day or two after that, right up until the awful day when the barber had been arrested.

He sometimes wondered what had become of the man. Was he cutting hair for the Nazis now? Or was it harder work that they made him do?

The barber had never come home again. Cornelius wondered, did they take him to a concentration camp?

He shrugged, who knows? At least the man was no longer betraying people.

In any case, Cornelius no longer had to surrender any of his pigeon eggs.

CHAPTER EIGHTEEN

One More Move to Make

R umors said that the Allied troops were getting much closer to the Netherlands. Now there was an atmosphere of expectation in the country, even excitement.

Sometimes it led to celebrations which angered the German soldiers. Often, they would come to break up these impromptu festivities, telling the people to go home, and shooting into the air to scare them away.

The people loudly exclaimed, "The Americans are coming! The Americans are coming!"

Things were soon to change.

The column of six German army trucks had left the town of Barneveld, and its chicken farms, far behind. They were headed back to The Hague. The wooded landscape around the town of Hoevelaken had gradually changed to meadows and open fields.

The sergeant and the sergeant-major on the first truck had been discussing what had occurred in the city of Barneveld.

Suddenly, the sergeant yelled, "Stop! Do you see that man on the bicycle? What's he doing all the way out here? He's the town clerk from Barneveld."

"It could be that he is fleeing his post," the sergeant-major said. "Let's stop him and see what he's up to."

"If he has left his position, perhaps he fears exposure."

"We'll take him in for questioning. I'll bet he cracks like an egg. They're bound to get some good information out of him."

Adrian noticed that the trucks had stopped and that the soldiers were getting off. When he realized that they were coming his way, he began to pedal his bicycle very quickly in the opposite direction. Sadly, he was no match for the running soldiers, and within a few hundred yards they'd caught him.

One of the soldiers picked up his bicycle. Two more held him by the arms and led Adrian back to the sergeant-major. "Well, well, look who we have here. It's the town clerk of Barneveld. Where are you going, my friend; and what are you up to?"

Adrian tried to stammer out a reply, but this time he had no ready answers.

"You're under arrest," the sergeant-major said. "Shall we go together to the head office in The Hague? There we can enjoy a nice interrogation. I think that, perhaps, you have something to hide. Clearly you're trying to escape something."

Adrian tried to protest. "I've done nothing wrong! I am simply going to see my sister."

"There's no sense in protesting," the sergeant-major shook his head. "You are coming with us."

When the trucks arrived back in The Hague, the sergeants went straight to Captain Wuerff to report on their unsuccessful raid, and their failure to apprehend Kees.

Adrian was taken to the jail and turned over to the interrogators. They soon found out that Adrian had been a member of the NSB, which was good for him. Unfortunately, he had made no significant contributions to the cause of the Nazis, which was not so good. The interrogators suggested that maybe now it was time that he did.

They asked Adrian directly about hiding places in and around Barneveld. As the town clerk, they were sure he would be able to provide information on such hiding places. After putting sufficient pressure on Adrian—not very much, as it turned out—he showed real eagerness to cooperate.

Adrian speculated that the pastor of the church might have taken in the seventy-two Jews from the chicken farm. His speculation was reported immediately to Captain Wuerff.

The next day, the six trucks roared off toward Barneveld once again. This time, they knew just where to find the Jews.

KEES AND FRANS had hidden at the chicken farm all night. In the morning, they climbed out of their hiding place, and found that the Jews who had escaped the chicken pen had been taken in by the pastor of the church. They went to see the pastor.

From the pastor, they learned that the trucks, and the platoon of soldiers, had left Barneveld. That was a great relief, but Kees and Frans were convinced that the Nazis would be back.

In part, this was because the pastor had mentioned that the town clerk had left town to go into hiding. The pastor said, "I'm afraid that Adrian cannot be trusted. His role as a traitor is sure to be discovered."

"The people you have here, sir, need to be moved to another hiding place, immediately," Kees said. "We believe the Nazis will return soon. If they do, then this time it's because they know where the people in your care can be found.

"We have to move fast. Frans and I will be going—there are three more hiding places in Gelderland. Once we've found the right one, we'll make arrangements to have your people moved."

"I'll tell them to be prepared," the pastor said, "to keep their belongings ready."

"Yes," Frans agreed. "Tonight, we'll make the move. We'll go now, to set things up. Pray that it all goes well. Hopefully the Nazis will take their time coming back."

Riding their bicycles at full speed through the woods, Kees and Frans knew they had three addresses to visit—and no time to lose. One of the most promising farms on the list had recently held a large group of Jews. They had just been moved to another farm in the province of Drenthe.

When the Resistance men arrived at the first farm, they were met by the farmer and his wife. The couple told them that they had no intention of hiding any more Jews.

"The strain on our family has been just too great," the farmer explained. "We need to recover. With the end of the war coming very soon, we feel we need to lay low."

"I'm very sorry to hear that," Kees said, "but we understand your position. Your help has been invaluable."

The men traveled to the second farm, where they were met with a similar reaction. "We're very glad that you came, Kees. But we're totally unprepared now. We haven't had any refugees here on the farm for the last six months.

"They were taken out by the Resistance, over the border to Switzerland. But it's been so long now that our spaces have been put back to work. We have nowhere left to shelter them."

Kees nodded his understanding. He and Frans mounted their bikes and prepared to move on.

"Wait, there may be something else that we can do."

"Tell me," Kees said, climbing off his bicycle.

"There's a place we know, far from here. It's out in the meadows, surrounded by trees. No German has ever gone there."

Frans looked at Kees. "Sounds good, right?"

"Whenever the Germans came," the farmer continued, "they always searched everywhere, and they never found a thing. We stayed friendly with them, and fed them; so I think we're on good terms. They should pass us by here, if they do return.

"So we can still help. We'll put them up at the place in the woods. It's about two miles from here, beyond our fields. I think they will be safe there."

"This is great news," Kees replied. "Tell me what it's like."

"Well, the only problem is, the place is not very big," the farmer said. "The group you have may be a bit too large. I suggest we go look it over, so you can see for yourself if it will work. If you approve, we'll be happy to take your people in."

"Excellent," Kees said. He looked at Frans, who gave a nod.

"Then we can take our horse and carriage," the farmer said, "and go now!"

When they arrived at the distant hiding place they found only a dilapidated, old stable. There were no amenities, no heating, a single tap for water, and a small outhouse.

"The people will be virtually on their own out here. It'll be a tight squeeze; but it's well hidden, so we know it is safe," the farmer explained. "But with so many, someone will have to dig a hole so they can empty the barrel from the outhouse."

As sparse as it was, Kees approved. In these final days of the war, the kind of accommodation was not so important. All that mattered was that the refugees remained safe from the Nazis.

"Now, we need a plan to get them all here," Kees said. "At the moment, the group is in Barneveld. There are too many to move them all by wagon. How far away is Barneveld? Do you think we can make it on foot?"

The farmer thought for a moment, then said, "It's only about eight kilometers away, which means a walk of about two hours. They should stay off the road and come through the woods, out of sight of any military vehicles. Yes, about two hours, I think."

"You're right, it's best that they walk," Kees said. "A farm wagon or carriage could catch the eye of the military."

"Can you go with us?" Frans asked, "We'll need a guide to bring the people through the woods. That way, no one gets lost, and we get them here in the fastest, most direct way."

The farmer nodded. "If I can jump on the back of your bike, you can take me there directly. But first, we have to go and warn my wife about what's going on. She can bring drinking water, food, and toilet paper out here while we're gone. Then all will be ready when we all arrive."

Their thighs burning from the effort, it took the men only half an hour to ride back to the church in Barneveld. Kees, Frans, and the farmer met with the pastor first, to go over their plan, and explain what the people could expect for accommodations.

"Is there anyone in the group who is unable to walk?" Frans asked. "Some may find a two-hour walk hard to manage."

The pastor nodded, "I'm afraid so. Not too many, I think."

"We'll have to arrange for some transportation then," Kees said. Turning to the farmer, he asked, "What do you think? Do you have anything we can use to move the less-capable?"

"We can use our haywagon. We'll stack hay bales around the edges and have the people sit in the middle. But, I wouldn't want to do that during the day. We should wait, and go when it is dark, just to be safe."

"Are we ready then?" Frans asked. "We should go down and explain to the poor people in the basement, to ease their fears." Kees nodded his agreement, stood up, and gestured to the pastor to lead the way.

The group of tired, fearful people bombarded Kees with a barrage of questions. "Wait, wait! Quiet, please," Kees said. "I'll explain exactly what's going to happen over the next few hours. We will take good care of you, and we'll get you to a place where no one can find you.

"We've just gone out to see your next hiding place. I'm afraid it's a bit . . . rustic. But safety and security are more important now than comfort.

"I'd like to see the hands of those who are unable to walk for two hours." Kees counted them, there were only eight. "Good! I'm happy to know that most of you can make it. We'll have a pleasant little hike in the woods today—far from any roads.

"Those eight who can't make the hike, you'll get to go on a nice little hayride." Even though it was well past Halloween, his little jokes brought some smiles to their faces. "Since the wagon has to use the roads, you'll go later, after dark.

"We have informants in the villages all around here. They can warn us of any oncoming military traffic, so we can leave the road if need be."

Now that they all had a plan to follow, the worry and fear among the crowd had eased. The faces that looked back at Kees were now set with determination.

"Ladies and gentlemen, let's get ready for a nice walk in the country. Stay close together, and please do not talk. This must be a quiet trip. After you arrive at our destination, you may talk all you want."

Kees and Frans took up their bicycles, and the farmer led the way. Every ten minutes or so, one of the men would mount up and pedal a few hundred yards ahead of the group, to be sure that no one else was in sight.

The walk was surprisingly pleasant, and it took place without incident. The group managed to stay concealed in the forests for the most part, crossing open ground only once. Kees said a silent prayer of thanks.

The people were glad to arrive at the battered old barn, and they expressed their relief by chatting joyfully. The farmer's wife had brought buckets of fresh water, along with some cups, and plenty of food. She showed them where to use the single faucet to wash their dishes, and themselves.

The people set to work taking care of each other, and making the old barn livable. If this was to be their home—for perhaps as long as two months—then they were fully prepared to make the best of it.

CHAPTER NINETEEN

Why the Jews?

As early as the 1920s, the Jews were blamed for the defeat of Germany in the first World War. A devastating post-war economic crisis and runaway inflation caused all kinds of anti-Jewish sentiment to flare up. German extremists forced the government to take away their citizenship, and they chased the Jews out of Germany.

In 1925, there were more than half a million Jews living in Germany. The great recession, from 1929 until 1932, hit Germany particularly hard, and the economic chaos resulted in the birth of the Nazi party.

The party fanned the flames of hatred for Jews, partly out of envy for their prosperity, and partly out of political calculation. After all, a scapegoat was needed—somebody had to be blamed for the miserable existence of the German people. Someone had to be a target for their rage. Many Jews, startled awake from their once peaceful existence, fled the country.

In 1933, tens of thousands of Jews immigrated to countries like the United States, Canada, and South America. This emigration was also the beginning of the Zionist movement, which would eventually establish a Jewish state in the British Mandate of Palestine. But the ancient Jewish dream of Israel was far from being realized, as the European home of the Jews descended into fanatical racial hatred.

Many Jews, those without the financial resources necessary to emigrate overseas, fled to the countries that surrounded Germany. Thousands of Jewish refugees flooded onto the roads that led out of the country.

With the elections in the fall of 1936, the so-called "Aryan nation" was born. The Jewish people of Germany were stripped of even their most basic rights, and the government began the confiscation of all Jewish shops, factories, and other commercial establishments. Soon, the Jews would even begin to lose their homes. And after that, it would only get worse. The hatred that the Nazi Party had stoked for the Jewish people had now become national policy.

As the influence of Germany grew, so too did its policies and attitudes spread all across central Europe. The same confiscations and brutalities took place on a large scale throughout the countries of Austria and Poland as well. It would not stop there.

A seventeen-year-old Jewish boy, by the name of Herschel Grynszpan, was living in Paris, and he was growing increasingly angry over the treatment of his fellow Jews. When he received an alarming letter from his sister in Germany, he decided that he'd had enough.

His sister wrote that their parents had been taken from the family home and ordered out of Germany. Without warning, they had been evicted. Without money, food, or drink, they were put over the border into Poland. Their parents were now helpless and in great trouble."

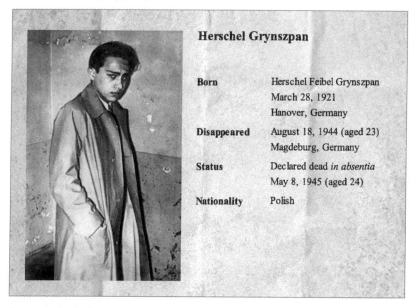

Herschel Grynszpan

Born	Herschel Feibel Grynszpan
	March 28, 1921
	Hanover, Germany
Disappeared	August 18, 1944 (aged 23)
	Magdeburg, Germany
Status	Declared dead *in absentia*
	May 8, 1945 (aged 24)
Nationality	Polish

Grynszpan just before his arrest in 1938.

Herschel was so enraged, that he bought a pistol and a box of bullets, intending to take some measure of revenge. He went to the German embassy in Paris, and asked to meet with an embassy worker. When Herschel was introduced to Ernst vom Rath, he raised his gun and shot him several times.

The embassy man was gravely wounded. Adolf Hitler himself sent his two best doctors to save vom Rath's life; but it was to no avail. Ernst vom Rath died two days later.

The news of the shooting appeared in papers all across Germany within hours. There would be hell to pay.

CHAPTER TWENTY

The "Kristal Nacht"

D uring the night of the 9th and 10th of November in 1938, a horrendous act of violence against the Jews took place. This was the very beginning of the long, dark period known as the Holocaust.

In Munich, a large number of Nazi leaders held a meeting to celebrate Hitler's 1923 coup to incorporate the Bavarian and Austrian areas into the Nazi movement. The coup—known as the Beer Hall Putsch—had failed, and the Nazi leaders continued to blame the Jews. The Minister of Propaganda, Joseph Goebbels, announced that the time was ripe to extinguish the influence of the Jews, to crush it—and them—once and for all. No more would these Jews be able to plot against the Nazis.

In all German-speaking territories, including Bavaria and Austria, the members were encouraged to take part in a pogrom against the Jews. Within hours after the announcement, riots had broken out in every city and town all over the country.

Thousands of Jewish homes, businesses, and properties were attacked or destroyed. Broken glass from the smashed windows of their shops and houses littered every street. The owners were brutally kicked and beaten, many until death. Hundreds of synagogues were desecrated and burned.

The rabbis were arrested along with many prominent Jews. Lawyers, doctors, and business owners were arrested by the tens of thousands and shipped to newly erected concentration camps. In the camps, they were beaten and abused and hundreds more died at the hands of the Nazis.

It was only the beginning.

These horrific pogroms came to be called *Kristallnacht* (the Crystal Night) or the Night of Broken Glass. Afterwards, many harsh and restrictive new laws were laid upon the Jewish community. The Jews further suffered demands for millions of Deutschmarks as fines for their "unpatriotic behavior."

The German government created the Central Department for Jewish Emigration, which encouraged Jews to get out of the country. This resulted in increased immigration by Jewish refugees to the surrounding countries.

After these horrific events, and the severe new changes in government policy, there were few Jews who wanted to remain in Germany. One country that was popular among the refugees was the Netherlands. At the border, they were stopped and identified. Sometimes, when they could not identify themselves, they crossed illegally. The Dutch people were very compassionate and tried to help as many as they possibly could.

The Netherlands was one of the few countries that welcomed these unfortunate people, at first. The Dutch government built special transit facilities to accommodate the Jewish refugees. As a result, Camp Westerbork was born.

What began as a kindness soon became a horror under the occupation of the Nazis.

CHAPTER TWENTY-ONE

Unintended Consequences

I n 1939, the Dutch government decided that they should build a camp for the Jewish refugees from Germany. The camp was built in a northern province of the Netherlands in an open field near the town of Westerbork.

As the camp filled up with Jewish refugees from Germany, Poland, and Austria, it developed in a way that resembled normal life in a small city. There was a theater, a school, a restaurant, and farms where the refugees were required to work. There was a certain freedom among the occupants.

The Germans attacked the Netherlands on May 10, 1940, and bombed the port city of Rotterdam for five days. Then, they demanded that the Netherlands government surrender unconditionally. In Camp Westerbork, many of the refugees felt that they had to leave the camp and escape the Netherlands. A large group of refugees took a train to the city of Zwolle, about 40 kilometers from Westerbork, intending to continue on to Rotterdam where they could then board a ship to England.

However, the train got no further than the bridge over the River IJssel. There, the rail bridges had been bombed into the

Camp Westerbork before the Nazi invasion, still with some relative freedom.

water. Unfortunately, all those who'd hoped to flee had no choice but to return to the camp the same day.

Even though Camp Westerbork was filled with Jewish refugees, it remained in the hands of a Dutch commander and was controlled by the Dutch state police, even after the Nazis had won control over the country. The rules changed and freedom was much more limited, but that was to protect the Jewish community. Up until July 1942, Westerbork was never called a concentration camp. It was a refugee community.

Then, the Nazis took over the camp.

In the two years since the war had begun in the Netherlands, Camp Westerbork had three commandants. The third, and last, was SS Obersturmfuehrer (First Lieutenant) Albert Conrad Gemmeker. From October of 1942, the Captain lived in a nice, quiet house at the entrance of the camp.

SS Obersturmfuehrer Albert Gemeker, Commander of Camp Westerbork, and the luxurious house that was built for the camp commanders.

It was the duty of the camp commander to keep peace and order among the prisoners of the camp. To promote this, Lieutenant Gemmeker created a school for children and a hospital. Workshops of all kinds kept prisoners employed, and he allowed the prisoners to perform in concerts and the theater to improve their morale. The small-town atmosphere of the former refugee camp was maintained.

However, security in the camp became stronger and harsher with every passing month. There was a tall barbed-wire fence, about seven meters high, behind which there was a deep ditch. At every hundred yards there stood a watchtower, with soldiers and machine guns that covered the entire camp.

While it was possible to escape, the consequences of escape were severe. Everyone close to the escapee's family and friends would be put on a transport train and sent immediately east to a concentration camp. For every person who escaped, ten prisoners were selected for transport. This harsh measure prevented many escapes.

Used to transport as many as 200 people at a time, some boxcars were equipped with guard compartments for a soldier with machine gun.

In Camp Westerbork, the prisoners were never hit or physically abused; they were treated as normally as was possible. This helped maintain the illusion that the camp was just a temporary home for refugees. But straight through the center of the camp there ran a railroad line, and everyone understood its purpose. Each Tuesday, an empty train arrived at the camp. With each train, a thousand prisoners were selected to leave. Their destination was the concentration and extermination camps deep in Germany and Poland.

CHAPTER TWENTY-TWO

Unscrupulous Discrimination

E va and Abraham Beem, sister and brother, were born in the city of Leeuwarden, in Friesland. After the invasion of the Nazis, their parents sent them into hiding in the country. They would live with a Christian family who was willing to foster them—and risk death, if caught. Eva was eight years old, and Abraham was just five.

The children lived undercover with the Hillebrandt family, as Linni and Jan de Witt. Eva and Abraham had friends and went to school there for three years. They were even allowed to write coded letters to their "aunt and uncle" (their parents).

Tragically, not every Netherlander was a patriot—some people, like the members of the NSB, happily collaborated with the Nazis. Some NSB-ers even accepted payment for revealing the identities of refugees and fellow Dutch citizens who were in hiding. In February, 1944, Eva and Abraham were apprehended at their hiding place in the town of Ermelo. Because their parents were in hiding far away, the children were sent to Camp Westerbork alone. Since the two had no family in the camp, they were declared to be war orphans and placed in the camp orphanage.

Abraham and Eva Beem, age 5 and 8, were sent into the country to live undercover as non-Jews. They survived and thrived for three years, until they were betrayed by the NSB.

After a few weeks in the camp, Abraham wrote a letter to his parents, who had moved to another hiding place. "How are you doing? With us everything is great, the food is good, and it is very cozy here."

Two weeks later, the children were shipped off to Auschwitz. Upon arrival they were immediately sent to the gas chamber. Eva was eleven years old, and Abraham was eight.

ON JUNE 12, 1942, a Jewish girl named Anne Frank wrote in her diary, "Now that the Germans are in charge in this country, misery has begun for the Jewish people." She had received the diary for her thirteenth birthday.

"The Nazis created hundreds of rules, laws, and regulations, on what we could not do," she wrote. "We always had to wear a

Star of David. We could not ride a bicycle. We could shop only at Jewish stores, which were controlled by the Nazis. We were not allowed to go to the theaters, swimming pools, or sports events.

"We could not be on the streets between 8 p.m. and 6 a.m. We could not even sit in our backyards at night! Living became so prohibitive that people said, 'I don't dare to do anything, because I'm afraid it might not be allowed.'"

A month later, the family moved into a small, hidden apartment. They lived there with another Jewish family for two years, never going outside, always in constant fear of discovery.

On August 8, 1944, Anne Frank and her family were arrested and sent to Camp Westerbork, now a concentration camp. They had been betrayed by NSB-ers in Amsterdam.

Because the Frank family had been caught in hiding they were labeled as "convict Jews" and confined in the punishment barracks. They were forced to work long, hard hours, usually at the dirtiest jobs available.

Her father said, "We had to work hard, but at night we were allowed to visit each other. It was a great relief for the children, since we were no longer in hiding. But we feared that sooner or later, we might be transferred to a concentration camp in Germany or Poland."

His fear came true four weeks later.

On September 3, 1944, yet another cattle train departed from the camp. This time, the Franks were aboard.

Otto stated, "On that horrible transport, we were locked up in a cattle wagon, and I saw my family for the last time. Each of us tried to be brave and not to give up."

It was the last train to depart from Camp Westerbork.

The destination was Auschwitz.

Margot and Anne Frank lived in hiding in Amsterdam with their family and others for several years until they were discovered. Anne's diary was later published as "The Diary of a Young Girl" and became one of the most well-known books in the world.

Nearly a thousand of the passengers survived the trip. Upon arrival at the extermination camp, over 500 were sent directly to the gas chambers. This included every child under fifteen years of age. The rest were selected for slave labor, where they would be worked until death. Anne was just a few months past her fifteenth birthday. She was one of the youngest marked for slavery.

A month later, Anne and her sister Margot were selected for relocation to the concentration camp at Bergen-Belsen. They were separated from their mother, Edith, who died shortly thereafter from starvation.

Anne and Margot survived Bergen-Belsen for four months. In March, 1945, a typhus epidemic raged throughout the camp and killed Margot. Anne died a few days later. She was not yet even sixteen years of age.

The war in Europe would end only two months later. Anne's father, Otto, was the only member of the family to survive.

FROM OCTOBER 1942 until April 1945, Commander Gemmeker was responsible for the transportation of approximately 80,000 Jewish people from Camp Westerbork to the concentration and extermination camps in the east.

After the war, Albert Gemmeker was sentenced to just ten years imprisonment in the Netherlands. In April of 1951, he was dismissed early and returned to Germany. He lived until 1982 and died of natural causes, at the age of seventy-five.

AN ASPIRING WRITER, Anne journaled about their life in hiding in her diary. After the war, it was discovered and published as *The Diary of a Young Girl.* It went on to become one of the most well-known books in the world, published in 60 languages, and was the basis for many plays and films.

CHAPTER TWENTY-THREE

Bringing a Final Warning

Kees and Frans had made plans to visit at least six more hiding places the next day. The news that the Germans were on their way again made the two Resistance men anxious to get to the hiding places in the Barneveld area. When the Nazis found no one in the church, they were certain to go mad and raid every farm in the area.

As fast as they could, the two friends pedaled from one farm to the other, just to warn the owners of the pending visit. Other Resistance groups, from cities like Utrecht and Apeldoorn, had been using these farms as well. Several of the farmers had hidden large numbers of Jews in the past. The farmers warmly welcomed the two Resistance men from The Hague. Each one told the men the same story, that everyone in hiding had moved on. As soon as Kees and Frans had delivered their warnings, they traveled to the next farm.

It was mid-day when the Nazi trucks arrived at the church in Barneveld. They pulled up on all sides of the building and the soldiers dismounted quickly to surround the church. Two sergeants pounded on the main entrance door, then burst into the sanctuary the moment the door opened. Other men crashed in through the back- and side-doors.

The pastor was pushed up against a wall, and with screaming voices they demanded, "Where are they? Where are the Jews?"

The pastor just shook his head, and cried out, "There is no one here! You can look for yourselves!" He gestured down a hallway. "Let me show you to the basement, right down there. Who told you that there are Jews hiding here? It's nonsense."

There followed a chaotic hour of screamed commands and running soldiers who destroyed anything in their way. Eventually, the soldiers returned to the sanctuary. They confirmed that there was indeed no one in the church.

Furious, the sergeants pushed the pastor into a corner and began to hit him, slapping first with open hands, then fists, and finally with the butts of their guns. "We know they were here! Where are the Jews? Tell us now!"

The pastor did not say one word. Finally, he collapsed under the blows and fell to the floor, unconscious.

The captain in charge finally commanded his soldiers to stop their torture. "Enough, you fools. How can you expect anything from a dead man?"

He called his sergeants together and ordered them to load up the men, then spread out and search every house, farm, and shop in the area. "They have to be somewhere close. Find them, or I will have you all shipped to the Russian front."

Over the next several hours, Barneveld suffered one of the worst *razzias* ever inflicted on a small town. Every shop, every house, every farm, was raided and searched. Shots were fired at random, furniture was knocked over, and rooms were ransacked. There was much screaming—by soldiers and by the frightened citizens. But in the end, nothing was found and there were no arrests made.

The captain and his sergeants were infuriated, growing dangerously frustrated at the stories and excuses told by the people whose homes they raided. The soldiers kept their heads down and avoided the wrath of their leaders by looking for more things to search or destroy.

At the same time, the citizens were growing angry and resentful. They knew that the occupation was coming to an end soon, and this brutal treatment was out of order. People had began to gather outside, voicing their outrage to each other. The town's policeman knew this would only bring trouble, so he moved from group to group, urging them to calm down. He breathed a great sigh of relief when the Germans finally loaded up and moved off in their trucks.

The column drove just a short distance outside of town, then stopped. The sergeants and their captain gathered alongside the road to discuss their plan of action.

One of the sergeants had executed many *razzias* in the larger cities. He said to the captain, "We're stirring up the entire population around here, sir. It will only make them hide their Jews even farther away.

"We should leave the town. Move at least ten kilometers out and raid the farms along the way. I'll bet we find one outside of town with a large group of Jews. What do you think, sir?" he asked the captain. His leader nodded in approval.

"One more thing. If we split our trucks into pairs, we can visit three farms at once, giving them no time to warn each other."

"That, sergeant, is a fine idea. Do it."

CHAPTER TWENTY-FOUR

The General Prepares for Life After the War

In the fall of 1943, General Habsberger took a short vacation from his post in the Netherlands. The General also took a break from collecting valuable works of art, priceless antiques, jewelry, and gold and silver stolen from museums and art galleries across the Netherlands. He felt that he'd worked hard during the occupation, and that he had accomplished relative peace in the country of Holland. He deserved a break.

Of course, there'd been struggles with the treacherous Dutch Resistance. He remembered the attack on the celebration at the ancient Binnenhof. He had collapsed in the failed gas attack. It had been a shock to the Germans to suffer such a well-organized attack. Fortunately, the cyanide concentration had been too low to kill any of the officers at the party. They had all recovered in a short time.

The Gestapo had taken revenge a few days later, simply by shooting one citizen in each and every street. The General had been dismayed by the bluntness of the tactic, and it had been a great bone of contention between him and the Gestapo leadership. The repercussions on the Dutch in The Hague would be tremendous. It would only fuel their Resistance.

The General was of the traditional military school, and disagreed with the killing of innocent civilians. He preferred to limit killing to the battlefield. When he had voiced his opinion, his fellow officers had shunned him for the longest time. The General had been isolated from their fellowship, and the parties the officers often held. It was just as well, he'd only had more time to complete his work.

General Habsberger looked forward to the end of the war. He expected it to come very soon. Even as far back as 1943, he had begun to make plans to live in abundance after the war.

With the Allies' invasion of Normandy in June of 1944, it had become all too obvious: Hitler had no chance of reaching his lofty goals. There would be no world-domination. Hitler's book, *Mein Kampf*, was no longer worth the paper it was printed on. The General had quietly disposed of his copy long ago.

With the war soon coming to an end, it was time to prepare for his return to civilian life. General Habsberger was still happily married and had three children back in the Swartzwald. He looked forward to spending more time with his family.

However, as a general, he well understood that he was likely to be tried by the Allies, and possibly punished for his time here in the Netherlands. This could not be—it would interfere with his hoped for plans. Habsberger felt that he had committed no real crimes during his service to the Reich, and he'd done nothing inhumane. He had simply done his duty. So, he refused to allow anyone, or any court, to stand in his way.

The slogans *"Befehl ist befehl"* (an order is an order) and *"Ich habe es nicht gewust"* (I did not know that) were sure to be useful.

THE GENERAL had taken his first vacation back in 1943, when the war was still going fairly well. Even then, he'd known the war could not last forever—whatever the outcome. So he'd begun his preparations. The General flew to Brazil, where his plan was to be realized. He began by negotiating for a fine piece of land. It was his in trade for a single, very valuable piece of stolen art.

Earlier that year, at an exhibition in the city of Apeldoorn, Habsberger had seen an object that he knew would provide him with a way out of this untidy war. Several paintings of Franz Hals were on display, some of them for the very first time.

A week after the exhibition, he ordered the sergeant and his platoon to close down the art museum . . . for reasons of security. The Dutch director, the curator, and all six of his staff were summarily dismissed. The men were sent off to labor camps, to avoid any troublesome complaints. The women were given a chance to work in his administration. After all, he was not a barbarian.

The closing of the museum was a shock to the population, and they protested angrily against it. This was of little concern. The general issued a declaration, which was pasted on the door:

> This museum will be closed for an indeterminate time. The paintings will be preserved and placed in a secure undisclosed location under the care of a professional curator.

The undisclosed location would be a confiscated villa of a former ambassador to the Netherlands in the town of Wassenaar. There was a particular painting that he had set his mind on owning. It was a seventeenth-century portrait of a woman which he swore could have been his own grandmother.

It was at that time that the General had met Haagendoorn, a Jewish art curator. The man had seen the writing on the wall. He offered to take care of the art and preserve it for any future plans after the war. Haagendoorn was a professional curator who was in love with the famous Dutch Masters. He did not care where the paintings went, only that they were cared for and preserved.

The only problem, Haagendoorn was a Jew.

When the general offered him protection and immunity, he had gratefully accepted a job as curator. He would remain a resident of the villa, where he was happy and willing to do anything that the General pleased. It was certainly better than the alternative. He was a bachelor now. His family had already been deported to a concentration camp.

Gradually, the collection expanded, as other objects of art, jewelry, antiques, precious metals, and diamonds were added to the ongoing "requisitions." Even then, the General still maintained honorable intentions concerning the art. Plans were being made to transfer at least some of the treasures to Berlin. However, the vacation to Brazil had altered his good intentions. When he returned from his trip, the plans for Berlin were shelved, and Habsberger intensified his confiscation of art.

In Brazil, the General had socialized with rich landowners. He had become enchanted with this attractive country, with its vast and uninhabited lands. Habsberger felt that the tropical forests of Brazil could be his sanctuary for the rest of his life.

One of the landowners had offered him thousands of acres on the Amazon River, in exchange for a particular painting—the one that so resembled the General's grandmother. At a banquet in the city of Belem, at one of Brazil's most prestigious hotels, the deal had been sealed.

With this prospect of land ownership in Brazil, the General had found a safe hideout for life after the war, both for himself and his family. Naturally, this affected his plans for the art that he had "requisitioned" from the Dutch museums. If the Nazis had stood a chance of succeeding with their plans, then most of the art would have found its way to Berlin. But the General was not an unintelligent man. So his plans changed.

The Brazilian landowners offered him more than just land. They could construct whatever buildings he might desire. More importantly, they offered protection to the General and his family. The costs to the General were minimal—only a few more of the precious paintings. The feudal, powerful, crooked landowners had found in the General a kindred spirit.

A week later, the General was back in the Netherlands, where he spoke to a tired submarine commander. He too had considered the idea of moving to Brazil after the war. He had no wish to rebuild a possibly devastated Germany. Unfortunately, the submarine commander had little in the way of resources he could use to make such a move. He did, however, have the command of a submarine. The commander was willing to do anything to partner with General Habsberger.

During the conversation, the General asked the commander if he was willing and able to deliver a large "package" to Belem, in Brazil. For his help, the General would make him a partner in the land and the compound that was soon to be built.

Thus, the submarine commander demonstrated his enthusiasm for inter-service cooperation as he became implicit in the escape of several officers of the German army. On his next patrol, while scouting the waters around South America for American and British freighters, the commander made a quiet diversion to the coast of Brazil. He delivered a package for the General, one that contained several paintings for the landowners.

The Amazon is over a dozen times the size of Germany. In the middle of thousands of square miles of jungle, a small Nazi compound would be very difficult to find.

The landowners were true to their word, and so construction began on an elaborate compound, deep in the Amazon jungles. The buildings would house as many as fifty people in comfort. By the fall of 1944, Habsberger had moved his wife and children to the completed settlement in the jungle of Brazil. They were well agreed that they could not find a better refuge for the end of the war. The General left his wife and children in Brazil and returned to the Netherlands to finish his plans.

It was now time to bring Haagendoorn in on the plot. After all, he needed the man to be able to sell their valuable treasures for the highest prices on the world market. It was important that the pieces showed no connection to the Nazi confiscations. In the postwar world, this could cause the prices to collapse, or the buyers to disappear.

Haagendoorn accepted the General's offer without a single moment's hesitation. Looted or not, the deal would allow him to continue working with his beloved art. It would also keep him out of the concentration camps.

Yes, Brazil would be good for him. He knew that, in time, it would be revealed that he had collaborated with the Nazis. It would be better to be on the other side of the world when that finally happened.

CHAPTER TWENTY-FIVE

Revisiting the Farms

K ees and Frans pedaled from farm to farm warning families that the Nazis were coming. "Let's stop at the farm where we brought the Jews from the church," Frans said.

"Yes, we'd better warn them that the Nazis may be on their way," Kees agreed. "Even this far away from town, I'm worried about them."

When the two resistance fighters turned into the driveway of the farm, they noticed that the grass on the way to the barn was crushed, showing lots of foot traffic, and even some tire marks. "We need to do something about those tracks. If the Nazis see this, they'll follow the trails straight to our people," Kees said.

"We'll tell the farmer to bring his cows into that field," Frans suggested. "They'll trample the tracks our people made."

"Let's keep our visit short. We don't want to get caught here."

The men left their bikes behind the opened barn door and walked inside. There were a dozen cows, softly lowing and mindlessly chewing their cud while they waited to be milked by the farmer and his wife. Surprised to see them again, the farmer asked, "Well, what brings you back so soon?"

"The Nazis are on their way out of Barneveld. They may stop here to search your farm again. They seem to have information that a large group of Jews is still in hiding in the area.

"We thought we should warn you. We saw tracks in your meadow, on the way to the barn. If the Nazis see them, they'll follow those tracks to find our people. Can you put these cows out there, so they'll trample the tracks?"

"We'll have to finish milking them, before we can put them outside," the farmer's wife replied.

"I'm afraid that may be too late. Please, you must do it now," Kees said urgently. "For your own sake, hurry!"

The farmer nodded and said, "Let's do it all together. Kees and Frans, you can help. If you untie them all, we'll start guiding them outside. It will take just a few minutes. When the first cow goes out, the others will follow."

At the change in their routine, it seemed as if the cows wore an odd look on their faces. They seemed to say, "Aren't you supposed to milk us first?"

The Nazi trucks had left the town of Barneveld and were fanning out across the countryside. The sergeant in charge of the first pair of trucks was fuming. He told his men, "Our lives and our careers are at stake here. If we find the Jews, we may return to our *heimat* (homeland) with honor. But if we don't, God have mercy. It will be the Russian front for us, or even worse, a one-way trip to a concentration camp."

The trucks turned into the driveway of the farm, passing a gate that led into the meadows. One of the soldiers pointed out to the sergeant, "Look at the grass, sir. It seems that a lot of traffic has passed through this field. And look, there's even a wagon trail going through there."

"We'll follow that trail and see where it ends," the sergeant said, "but let's first search the farm itself."

As the soldiers were jumping down from the trucks, the door of the stable opened and a small herd of cows came walking out, led by the farmer and his wife. The sergeant approached the farmer and ordered him to stop. "You will leave the cows and open your house. We have orders to search this place." The farmer said nothing and continued to lead his cows out into the trampled meadow.

"Halt!" the sergeant repeated in a commanding voice, "or I will shoot!" To emphasize his command, he raised his gun into the air and fired a warning shot.

The startled cows broke and ran in every direction, mooing wildly. The surrounding soldiers burst out in laughter at the ensuing chaos. As the last of the frightened cows came galloping out of the stable, it ran into a group of soldiers. Some of the men tumbled to the ground, while others made a run for the stable.

They did not see the two men who slipped out of the stable as they quietly closed the door on the other side. "There's only one place we can hide where it will stink so bad that the soldiers won't even look." Kees pointed at a big steel hatch at the side of the stable. "In there. Open it and get in quickly, no matter what you see or smell."

The two men jumped into the cow dung cellar, where they felt the sudden warmth of manure and were overwhelmed by the potent scent of ammonia. Luckily, the cellar had been emptied fairly recently, and they could feel a concrete floor, just two feet beneath the surface of the dung.

Kees pulled the steel hatch back into place and let out a big sigh. "I think we'll be safe here, unless we choke from the smell."

They sloshed through the dark slurry, until they felt a concrete wall at the far side, opposite the hatch.

"What a person will do to save the lives of Jews," Kees said. "But, how and when will we be able to get out of here?"

"We'll just have to stay here and listen," Frans answered, "to hear when the trucks leave with the soldiers."

Methodically, the soldiers went through the farm in search of the hidden Jews. They climbed up to the attics and down in the cellars, opened closet doors, and went through the bedrooms, the kitchen, and every other space they could find.

Then, they went through the outbuildings, the stables, and even the outhouse; but they found no one. They even knocked over the stacks of hay bales to make sure there were no hidden spaces inside.

The men came together after their search to surround the sergeant. A corporal announced, "Nothing, sir. There is no one hiding here."

A soldier pointed back towards the trampled grass behind the meadow gate and asked, "What about that trail, sir? Should we follow it?"

The sergeant nodded and ordered his soldiers back onto the idling trucks. "The gate looks too narrow for the trucks. Knock the fence down and drive through." A truck engine revved loudly as if in anticipation.

"Leave some men behind to wait in the barn, just in case anyone shows up. I need two volunteers." Two soldiers dutifully raised their hands. "You, and you, go!"

The farmer and his wife were forced onto a truck, in between a pair of soldiers. The farmer bowed his head and prayed softly, "Lord, have mercy on those in the barn."

One of the soldiers heard the prayer and yelled, "What do you mean by that?"

"I mean the soldiers, of course," he farmer answered. "Who else would I mean, the cows?"

In moments, the trucks had plowed through the gate, and the surrounding fence. They started across the meadow, following the trampled trail, on their way to the hidden, dilapidated stable.

At the farm, one of the soldiers who had stayed behind, went walking around the barn. As he rounded the corner, he called for his comrade, "Look at this! You know, I used to be a farmer in the Schwartzwald (Black Forest) back home. Wherever there is a barn or a stable, there is a dung cellar. Let's look inside and see if they've used it to hide people."

The ex-farmer opened the hatch and they were assaulted by the ammonia-tinged stench of the dung. Quickly they slammed the hatch closed again. "*Ach!* No one, not even a dirty, hunted Jew, could hide in that foul stink," one of them remarked.

Two men, hiding against the back wall inside, cowered from the light coming into the cellar. They cringed when they heard the words, and sighed with relief when the hatch slammed shut.

"That was the closest call of the entire war," Kees whispered.

"Lucky we didn't climb out when we heard the trucks leave," Frans replied.

"I wonder why they left these two Krauts behind?"

CHAPTER TWENTY-SIX

The Arrests

A t the old stable, the farmer and his wife were wondering about the two soldiers as well. She whispered into her husband's ear, "I wonder where Frans and Kees have disappeared to? They must have gone out the back door of the barn, but there are no trees or bushes out there that are thick enough for them to hide in."

The farmer nodded, and bit his lip worriedly as he wondered where they'd gone. Then he looked up at his wife sharply as a sudden realization set in. "The bicycles!" he whispered, "Where are their bikes?"

"Oh, my goodness," his wife held her hand to her mouth, as if she wanted to put their words back in. She looked at her husband in fear. "They were behind the barn door!"

A soldier noticed the couple's lowered heads and shouted, "You two! No talking!" The farmer and his wife sat quietly. They had more to worry about now than Frans and Kees.

At the same time, the two soldiers at the farm walked round the front of the barn and noticed the two bicycles, lying partially concealed by the big barn door. They just stood there looked at them, and one of the men wondered, "Weren't we looking for two guys on bicycles around here?"

The other one nodded and said, "Yes, I believe we were. Do you think these bikes could be theirs?"

"They could still be around here somewhere. If we find them, we might get a few days of leave for catching them."

WHEN THE TRUCKS reached the thicket and pulled to a stop, the sergeant looked at the rickety, old stable and thought, *Nobody would be hiding in that old thing.*

But then he saw a flash of movement inside. He shouted to his men, "Surround the place, quickly! Shoot anyone who tries to run!"

"*Haende hoch!*" the soldiers yelled while they rushed into the dilapidated stable. The Jews inside were horrified to see the squads of soldiers come charging into the building. In terror, they raised their hands high. Some of them began to pray, "Lord, please have mercy on us."

Two young men tried to make a break for it. Shots rang out as soldiers ran after them. Luckily, both young men dropped to the ground before either was hit. The soldiers picked them up roughly and dragged them back to the trucks.

A sergeant shouted a command, "Load them up!" One of the soldiers repeated him, "All of them, on the trucks!"

The soldiers began pushing the people out of the stable and onto the trucks. On one of them, the farmer and his wife reached down to help pull them up.

Two more trucks rolled into the area, and in short order all four were overloaded with terrified Jews. The soldiers squeezed on, or stood on the running boards and held on as all four trucks drove back to the farmhouse.

THE TWO SOLDIERS who had remained behind approached the sergeant as he climbed down from the cab. "Sir, we have a mystery that needs to be solved. What do you want us to do?"

They told him about their find of the two bicycles. "Initially, we were looking for two men on bicycles, which leads us to think that the two men are still here, still somewhere in hiding."

"I will leave four more soldiers here with you," the sergeant said softly. "Hide yourselves inside, and stay clear of the windows, all of you. Don't walk around. Just be quiet and watch. If they are here, in time they will reveal themselves.

"After they've heard us leave, just wait it out until you catch them. When you do, tie them up, and wait for a truck to return. I'll leave a truck down the road, and have a soldier walk back to check on you in a few hours."

Before the trucks departed, the sergeant called the soldiers together and announced, "Gentlemen, congratulations on a successful raid! Captain Wuerff will be pleased. Now move out!"

When the men had reboarded the trucks, he raised his hand and signaled to the convoy: Go!

"The Captain will be even more pleased, when we have our last two fugitives," one of the remaining soldiers said softly to the others. "Take up your positions. But do it quietly."

THE TWO MEN in the dung cellar heard the truck engines start. They listened as the sounds of the trucks faded away. "Let's hope they don't return again," Kees whispered. "But to be sure, we'll wait another hour in this stinking hole."

"And let's hope they didn't find the Jews in the stable," Frans quietly replied.

The six left-behind soldiers had spread out and positioned themselves silently. Each one made sure he overlooked the entire farmhouse and outbuildings.

They communicated with each other through whispers and hand signals. The men with watches synchronized them to the grandfather clock in the house. That way, they could all hear the chimes.

The next time it rang was 2:00, they checked their watches to be sure they showed the same time. They had been in position for forty minutes. They had agreed to wait for two hours.

When the clock chimed three times, they realized they had been waiting over an hour and a half. It looked as if time was running out on them.

FRANS AND KEES had heard the chiming of the clock, too. It had been well over an hour. They decided it had been long enough. It was time to make their move and get out of the dung.

"It seems that they're gone now," Kees said. "Hopefully they won't return."

"I hope they didn't take our bikes," Frans said. "Let's see if we can find a hose and rinse ourselves off. I can't see us pedaling around with all this dung on our clothes."

When the men opened the hatch and climbed out, they were momentarily blinded by the sun, having been in complete darkness for hours. They walked around the barn and found a hose that was used to wash the cow dung into the cellar. After spraying each other down, Kees and Frans were laughing and feeling a good deal better. They coiled the hose back up and headed for their bicycles. Kees said, "Come on, let's go."

They were pulling their bicycles out from behind the barn door, when the men heard the sound of rushing footsteps. They were suddenly surrounded by a half dozen soldiers, rushing in from every direction. Guns drawn, several soldiers yelled, "Halt, halt! You are under arrest!"

The soldiers were smiling at each other now. They seemed exhilarated at their catch. Holding Kees and Frans at gunpoint, they tied their hands together.

A corporal turned toward one of the other men, and said, "Go get the truck."

CHAPTER TWENTY-SEVEN

Van Gend & Loos:
The Nazis Took It All

Before the war, Van Gend & Loos was a package delivery company with headquarters in The Hague. It was a proud and innovative company which delivered packages and larger shipments all across the Netherlands.

They made their deliveries with great horse-drawn wagons which were pulled by beautiful Clydesdale draft horses. The company had gigantic stables in the middle of The Hague just underneath the central train station. Freight that arrived by train was unloaded at the depot above and lowered into the gigantic garage by means of a large elevator.

The great building had been constructed to house all of their wagons, large and small, as well as the mountains of daily freight to be delivered throughout the entire country. When the wagons were loaded with freight, a span of horses was brought in from the stables and hitched to the wagons. Those special horses were well-fed and groomed, brushed lovingly by specially-trained horse keepers. It was a spectacular sight indeed to watch as a six-span transport left the garage and passed by on the street.

Hundreds of beautiful Clydesdale horses from Van Gend & Loos were confiscated, then killed for their meat, and shipped to Germany in ice wagons.

When the Nazis occupied the Netherlands, they put the Van Gend & Loos company out of business completely. They confiscated the buildings and the stables, as the Reich would be controlling trade, and the citizens would no longer need that form of transportation.

At first, the proud Clydesdale horses were to be used for the German military. But with the collapse of commerce, the great number of animals became a serious burden for the army. The horses were just too costly to feed. It was more important to keep German soldiers and civilians alive.

An "efficient" solution was found for both problems.

A special group of butchers was brought in from Germany. Every day, the horses were slaughtered, and the carcasses turned over to the butchers for processing. The meat was valuable to the German citizens so it was packaged, frozen, and shipped in ice

143

wagons back to the *Mutterland* (motherland). More than five-hundred horses were killed in a matter of two months.

Now that the problem with the horses had been solved, the Nazis turned their attention to the Van Gend & Loos buildings themselves. Dutch men were plucked from the streets to be slave laborers, then ordered to clean out the stables. They were to be prepared for a different breed of animal—captured Jews. The famous buildings of the company had been designated for use as temporary concentration camps.

In the garage, the great wooden carriages were dismantled by the laborers, to separate the wood from the steel—the Germans would make use of everything first. The wood was cut into small pieces, and loaded into cheap burlap bags. The bags would be sold to the Dutch citizens for firewood. The steel was melted down and sent to Germany for use in their production of war material.

Captured Jews were marched into the buildings at street level, and kept in the stables for a short time. When a transport train arrived, the people were brought up to the train platforms directly above the stables. The freight elevators made it an efficient operation. There, the Jews were loaded onto the cattlecars, filling them to the brim.

It was to the former Van Gend & Loos stables, that seventy-two Jews, rounded up at a farm in Gelderland, had been brought.

It had become Captain Wuerff's special holding place. He was hell-bound to finalize the annihilation of the Jews, even if he had to do so himself. While he was at it, he would do away with some of the traitors who had been helping the Jews these last four-and-a-half years.

CHAPTER TWENTY-EIGHT

"Oranje Hotel" (The Jail)

When the Germans occupied the Netherlands on May 10, 1940, they began to use the prison in the town of Scheveningen. They even gave it an ominous new name, the German Research and Punishment Prison. Over time, it would be known more informally as the Oranje Hotel, as a taunt of the royal family for the number of Resistance fighters that passed through.

The first Dutch citizens that were arrested were any and all members of the Resistance that could be found (or betrayed by the NSB). All Communists in the Netherlands were also rounded up and locked away in this prison, until they could be transported east to concentration camps.

Several members of the Dutch Resistance were tortured to death by the *Sicherheitsdienst* (Security Service). Their nightmarish deaths were simply classified as "research" or "punishment."

Very few prisoners ever managed to escape the prison. Late in the war, the Resistance staged an attack on the prison which failed dramatically (see *Resistance on a Bicycle*, Ch. 57). The attack cost the lives of seventeen members of the Resistance, all brutally executed.

Here in the dunes of Waalsdorpervlakte, more than 250 Dutch citizens (most from the Resistance) were executed. On May 10, an annual memorial is held.

During the war, more than 25,000 people were imprisoned in the Oranje Hotel, primarily for "crimes" involving the Resistance. These crimes could be anything from listening to a radio or destroying records in a city hall to attacking German soldiers directly. Many thousands were sentenced with transportation to the labor camps or concentration camps.

The prisoners were interrogated on a twenty-four hour basis, deprived of food, drink, sleep, and even from daylight—anything a human being needed to live. The tactics were simple, brutal, and usually unsuccessful. Once the Nazis were finished with their interrogations, the prisoners were transported to work camps or concentration camps, never again to return to their country or their families. Some never even got that far.

Over 250 people were sentenced to death and taken to a place in the dunes called the Waalsdorpervlakte. There, the prisoners were summarily executed.

The official entrance of the Scheveningen prison, or Oranje Hotel (top) in contrast to the exit door for the prisoners on their way to execution.

"Death cell" 601: once a Resistance fighter was sentenced here, death was hours away.

Once people passed through the entrance gate of the Oranje Hotel, they were doomed, one way or another.

When a person was sentenced to death, he was put into the death cell, number 601, for no more than twenty-four hours. A prisoner's final isolation in that cell was part of their conviction and punishment.

Next to the main entrance was a small door, *het Poortje*, that was just wide enough for one man to pass through. From there, the prisoner boarded a truck and was taken to the execution site.

IT WAS TO THIS PRISON that Kees and Frans had been brought for their interrogation. They had been awarded a special status, one condemned to extreme interrogation and torture.

The two brave resistance men were put into separate cells, right next door to each other. The cells were solid, so closed off and isolated that it was impossible for the men to communicate with each other. However, once an interrogation began, the door was left open by the Gestapo, so the two men could hear each other being tortured.

For several days, Kees and Frans suffered the pains inflicted upon them and refused to give up any information. This only enraged their tormentors. They were desperate for information on the hiding places of Jews and other Resistance members.

Captain Wuerff visited the jail each day, eager to reap what he thought would be a quick and easy confession. Every day when Wuerff inquired as to the results, he was disappointed.

The Captain grew increasingly irritated that the interrogators had not learned anything of importance to the Reich. He threatened the tormentors with rapid new postings to the eastern front. "I want answers! Or you'll soon see the *bolsheviks* up close!" This only encouraged them to redouble their efforts.

The cell doors of the Oranje Hotel. The doors were often left open during interrogations, so that the other prisoners could hear and be terrorized as well.

For five days, the Resistance men suffered brutal beatings and diabolical tortures; and for five days, these terrible torments had yielded nothing of value to Captain Wuerff.

Kees awoke at the noise of his cell door swinging open. He lay prostrate on the floor, bloodied and broken, ready to die; but still he was determined not to give in to their savage treatment. The Gestapo men hauled him up and resumed their work. Kees remained stubbornly silent.

Frans suffered another gruesome round of beatings, and he remained silent as well. But as his tormentors prepared for their next session, he finally cracked and said, "Please, no more. I will give you a list of hiding places. But first, we need a day of rest. Please. I'm too punch-drunk to write a list now."

Reluctantly, Frans' tormentors gave him a half day of rest, but they promised no such treatment for Kees. He was a stubborn Dutchman who refused to talk, and they were determined to change that.

One of the interrogators had a short whip on a wooden handle, and he used it with awful enthusiasm. With every question he asked, he would whip Kees fiercely. They bloodied and mutilated him until he no longer responded. When they finally left the cell, Kees lay on the floor in a fetal position, close to dying.

The next time that Captain Wuerff visited the prison, he was surprised and pleased to hear that they had some answers. Frans had finally surrendered a list of fifteen addresses, fifteen hiding places for Jews.

The following day, Wuerff ordered six trucks, each manned with a dozen armed soldiers, to go out on a search mission. He told the captain commanding the platoon to visit each address twice, over a time span of two hours.

"Search each address thoroughly," Wuerff had instructed. "If you find no one in hiding, look for clues. Things like more than the usual amount of garbage, tracks in the grass, and so on.

The platoon commander saluted, then left to gather his men. "Remember what we saw in Barneveld," he told them, once they had assembled. "Look for anything out of place, anything out of the ordinary. People may be hidden in barns or stables that could be miles away from a farm."

The sergeants who had been listening nodded their heads. "Yes, sir," one of them said, "But how do we see a second visit giving us better results?"

"We're creating a false sense of security," the platoon captain explained. "Be gentle at first. Don't tear the place up. When you leave with no results, thank the owners politely for their cooperation. It will make them feel relieved, and less suspicious."

"Yes, sir," the sergeant said, "But I still don't see how that helps us."

"If they are hiding Jews, they may come out after you've left to hear what happened," the captain continued. "Then, on the second visit, when your truck rolls in again, they will panic. Their faces will give them away."

CHAPTER TWENTY-NINE

Where are the Husbands?

It had been two days with no message at all from her husband, and Johanna was panicked. She made a visit to Frans' wife, who lived just one street over. Arriving in great distress, Johanna burst into tears when she heard that Frans had not come home either.

"Now, what do we do?" Johanna asked. Neither woman had any idea where to go for help.

Anna asked, "What about the Resistance group?"

"Yes, good!" Johanna brightened. "We'll go and visit their contact. We'll ask him to list every place that our husbands were sent over the past few days."

"We already know they were in Gelderland, near Barneveld. The Resistance man should know the names of the contacts at the farms. Hopefully, they will be able to find our husbands."

"We'll go right away."

The two women walked out of the house on Drebbel Straat, and hurried off to meet the Resistance man. They never noticed the two men in plain clothes that followed them about a hundred yards behind.

It was a quick walk, just a kilometer to the Heeren Straat, in the neighboring town of Rijswijk. The women found the house of Willem van Eik with no trouble, knocked, and were let inside. The men who'd followed them ducked into a shadowy hallway across the street, where a stairway led to several apartments.

Willem led his guests into a comfortable sitting room, and he listened patiently to the story the ladies had to tell. He shook his head with compassion, "Oh, no. I was afraid this would happen sooner or later. We've heard that some awful *razzias* took place in Gelderland.

"The Nazis have targeted many farms, searching for Jews in hiding. A cruel SS officer, by the name of Captain Wuerff, has ordered a last-ditch roundup. He is also the man who has been trying to arrest your husbands for hiding the Jews."

As Willem was talking, he glanced out a window and asked, "Johanna, have you been followed here?"

"Followed? Oh my, I'm sorry, but I don't know."

"I see two men, not in uniform, standing in a hallway across the street. They are casually looking our way. If they're in civilian clothes, then they're members of the SD (*Siecherheitsdienst*). They're even worse than Gestapo, or Captain Wuerff himself.

"You know, this could be a good sign. It shows that they're still after Kees and Frans. Perhaps, they have not yet found or arrested your husbands. We'll need to put them to a test."

Willem crossed the room and stood out of sight, next to the window. He offered a hand to Johanna, "My dear, will you please stand behind the curtains here, and carefully observe what happens next?" Johanna got up from her chair and stood beside him. Willem clasped hands behind his back and began pacing across the room, directly in front of the window, as he spoke.

"I am going to send two boys out on the street. One will go in one direction and the other, in the opposite direction. I need to know if the men split up to follow both boys. If they do, we have a problem."

Willem called upstairs, and a couple of boys soon appeared in the doorway to the sitting room. He gave them instructions, and they disappeared. The front door could be heard as it opened and closed.

Through a crack in the curtains, Johanna watched out of the window. "Yes. Okay, the men are splitting up. They're following the boys."

"Well, we do know something now," Willem announced. "It seems that they are still looking for Kees and Frans. . . ."

"Wait a minute," Anna interrupted. "Why then, haven't they come home yet?"

"Remember, your husbands could simply be in hiding some-where, waiting for the right moment to move, while you worry yourselves over nothing. I will send two men to Gelderland to have a look around."

"But that could takes days," Johanna protested. "What are we to do until they return? Just sit and wait?"

"No, no. We will do some investigating of our own." Willem stroked his chin as he thought, "It will be dark soon, curfew is approaching. We can use that to our advantage. . . ."

"Why? What are you thinking?"

"Well, we haven't used the ambulance lately," Willem mused, "so I'm thinking that we might take it out for a drive."

Anna and Johanna exchanged puzzled frowns.

"If you ladies will stay here for a while, I'll hop on my bicycle for a quick errand. I have to go out to the Ypenburg Airport, and see if the ambulance is operational. If it is, we'll need to make a few preparations. I'll be right back."

Willem could be heard rolling his bicycle out the back door. They heard the sound of the door closing. Willem pedaled away on his bicycle, taking the secret way through the backyard. Just in case he was stopped, he carried papers in his pocket that proved he had worked his required four hours that day.

The two women began to relax a little. Johanna was feeling better about the situation already, knowing that they would soon take action to find their husbands.

Willem returned in less than an hour. "All is good," he said. "Now that it's curfew, we can't be out on the streets. But with the ambulance, we can go anywhere. Barneveld is at least six hours away by bicycle. The ambulance, can get us there in two.

"Here's what we'll do. Anna, you will be the patient. I have some papers that allow for the transport of a female to the clinic in Amersfoort. That's close to the area where we're looking for your husbands.

"Johanna, you will be disguised as a nurse, and ride with our patient. As the ambulance driver, I will be dressed as a soldier. I have everything we need for this operation out in my workshop. The ambulance is parked there now, too.

"We're unlikely to be stopped at any roadblocks. If need be, I'll turn on the siren as we approach. They always let us through quickly that way."

This was the first time that the women were to play an active role in the work of the Resistance. They were quite enthusiastic about it, until Johanna realized that she had left her son Cornelius at home alone. "Just a minute," she said desperately, "what about my son? I can't leave him at home by himself."

"I will send one of my boys, Harry, to stay with Cornelius until we're back," Willem offered. "You'll have nothing to worry about at home while we're on our mission."

Two hours later, the ambulance passed through Utrecht. As they approached each roadblock they had only to switch on the siren, and they were waved on through without stopping. The town of Barneveld was nearing quickly.

Through the little window that connected the cabin to the rear, the driver told the nurse that he intended to visit the town-hall of the village first. He would check with the town clerk and see if any Nazi visits had occurred in the past few days.

"The clerk lives right next door to the town hall," Willem said. "In fact, I've spoken to him before, when we were looking for possible hiding places. He was very helpful."

As they rolled into Barneveld, they saw no trucks or soldiers, which was very encouraging. As late as it was, naturally the town hall was closed. Willem checked the house next door. Unfortunately, the clerk did not answer his doorbell.

"There is a chicken farm that we could check," Willem said as he climbed back into the driver's seat. "It's a safe hiding place, and I know the owner. He built a very large hiding place under one of the chicken houses. He and his wife have hidden a great many people from the Germans."

When the ambulance reached the farm, they saw that it was completely dark. Not a single light burned, either inside or out. Nobody came outside to meet them, and no one reacted to the knocks on the doors.

"This is very odd," Willem said. "Now, who can we try next?"

"Perhaps, the pastor of the church?" Johanna asked, "If anything has happened here, he would be the one to know."

As with the other stops, they found the church shrouded in darkness. Willem knocked at the door of the vicarage, but there was no answer. So they tried banging on the main door of the church. Much to their surprise, it gave way, swinging wide open at their touch.

The three of them—nurse, patient, and driver—walked into the shadowy chapel.

"This is very odd," Johanna said, "don't you think?"

"Shush," Anna said, "I think I hear something."

Out of the darkness, they heard a faint voice, "Help me. I'm here on the floor . . . by the altar."

Anna retreated to the doorway and groped for a light switch. The chapel was suddenly bathed in light, and they saw the pastor lying on the ground. Clearly, he was seriously wounded. The three of them rushed toward the altar.

When the pastor saw Willem approaching in his Nazi uniform, he panicked and prayed, "Please, God. No! No more of them!" Then he saw the German nurse and asked, "*Bitte, helfen sie mir und halt meinem bluetung.*" (Help me, and stop the bleeding, please.)

Johanna answered in Dutch, "*Wij zijn Hollanders, van het verzet.* (We are Dutch, from the Resistance.) Yes, sir, I can help you, but I have no bandages. Do you have any in the church?"

The pastor nodded, "In the green room, behind the stage, there is a closet that holds all kinds of medical supplies."

When the pastor was cleaned up, bandaged, and out of danger, they helped him up and sat him in a pew. "Are you feeling a little better now?" Johanna asked.

"Yes, thank you. But who are you, my good Samaritans? And why on earth are you in German uniforms? It makes no sense."

"Please, tell us what's happened here," Anna said. "The town clerk wasn't home, and we did not see one person in town. Now we find you wounded here in church. Was there a raid?"

The pastor told them all that happened in the past two days. "I advised the town clerk to leave town, and go into hiding somewhere. I felt sure that Adrian would be arrested. And if he were, he would be forced to give up anything he knew about hiding places in the area.

"Several farmers have already been taken by the Nazis. The Germans have come back twice—the second time to hold a town-wide *razzia*. But as far as I know, they never found our Jews.

"At one point, we had seventy-two staying here in the church. But they were in and out within about four hours. I don't know where they took them," the pastor finished.

"Where who took them?" Willem asked.

"Who? Well, the Resistance men, of course."

"Pastor, can you tell us what they looked like?"

He described the two men, and explained that they'd arrived on bicycles.

"Frans!" Anna said excitedly.

"And Kees!" Johanna echoed. The pastor nodded.

"Do you know where they are now?"

This time he shook his head. "The last I saw them was when they took our large group of Jews to another farm about 10 kilometers away. They went on foot, in the middle of the night."

"Do you know the name of the farm? Or the owner's name?"

"I believe it was the farm of Teun and Marianne De Ruyter."

"That's great," Willem said, "Can you guide us there?"

"In this condition? No, I couldn't possibly walk a single kilometer, much less ten."

"We have a German ambulance. We can take you."

"A German ambulance," the pastor repeated in awe. "Where, and how did you get that?"

"The tools of our trade," Willem answered with a sly smile.

"Come, let's get to the farm," Johanna urged them. "Quickly, we have no time to lose."

A kilometer away from the De Ruyter farm, the ambulance passed two oncoming German trucks. They could not tell if the trucks held any passengers. Willem said, "I wonder if they had anything to do with the raid?"

"They could very well have been part of it," The pastor nodded. "There were dozens of German trucks, more than I've ever seen at one time before."

As the ambulance passed the trucks, Willem flashed his lights and waved a hand outside the cabin. The trucks sped away, recognizing the ambulance as one of their own.

"Another farm in total darkness," Willem remarked, as they drove up the long driveway. They climbed out of the ambulance and walked toward the seemingly deserted house.

"Not even a single light lit," the pastor agreed. "This is not a good sign."

Out of the darkness walked a retarded farmhand. He was crying loudly. Johanna approached him and put her arms around the young man. Sobbing, he said to the group, "They're all gone. All gone. So many trucks."

Dreading the answer, Johanna asked, "Who's gone?"

"Everyone. Everyone from the barn in the field. They're all gone. Nobody left, not one," he said in between sobs. "Not my boss, not his wife. Even the two men with the bikes. Gone. What can I do, what can I do?"

Johanna and Anna were stunned. Their husbands had been arrested—and so close to the end of the war!

Suddenly, Johanna cried out in a panic, "Oh God, no! My son! Was he with them? Was my little boy with them? Oh, not my son too!"

"No, no. He's fine," Anna said, as she put her arms around Johanna. "You left Cornelius at home, remember?"

"Oh, thank God! Thank God, that's true," Johanna replied, hugging Anna back. "You're right, of course. I'd forgotten that Kees left him home this time."

"Let's go back to the city. Can we go home now? I need to see my son."

CHAPTER THIRTY

The List . . . and Desertion

F rans had given in. He'd supplied his tormentors with a list of authentic addresses. As a result, they had stopped torturing him, for the time being. Frans curled up on the hard cot in his cell and tried to rest. At least no one was beating him.

They had stopped beating Kees for the moment as well. The men showed the list to Kees, who nodded sadly. "Yes, these addresses are accurate," he said. "All are homes where we have been hiding Jews." He sighed, and let his head hang low.

The interrogators left Kees cell, and the guard pulled the door closed and turned a key in the lock. Kees breathed a welcome sigh of relief then, and felt shooting pains along his ribs. Were they broken? Probably. This was not shaping up to be a very good day.

On the brighter side, Kees knew Frans, and he knew those addresses too. Frans had given them places where once the Jews had been in hiding, but only the empty ones. No one would be found in any of them.

It was a clever idea, really. Kees wished he had thought of it himself. It might have saved him a few beatings, not to mention a few ribs. This was one of Frans' better ideas, because the Nazis couldn't blame him, once they found out that there were no more Jews in those hiding places. As a prisoner, how could he have known otherwise?

A pair of sergeants rounded up two dozen troopers. They loaded them up into four trucks and rolled out. The men were excited, but less because it was a final round up, and more because it got them out of the barracks and off guard duty for the day.

The sergeants told them that a successful raid would be good for them. It would please the officers in charge. *Yeah, maybe*, they thought to themselves.

After visiting the first few farms, the men realized that the list had indeed been accurate. There were clear signs that Jews, or somebody, had lived in these homes. Unfortunately, they were no longer there.

At each farm, the men were told the same story. The owners no longer had any people in hiding. They had all been moved to other places farther out in the country. A pattern seemed to be developing.

After the first ten addresses were visited, and all had turned up empty, the soldiers became wary. They began to complain. Were they going to be blamed for their lack of results? They seemed to have more fear of their superiors than of the enemy.

After a dozen farms, they stopped the trucks in a field, joining up with the captain in charge of the operation. It was time to report in. The officer and his sergeants gathered a short distance away from the trucks, out of hearing range of the men.

The first sergeant made his report. "Nothing, sir. Twelve farms so far, and not a soul on one of them."

"Yes, sergeant," the captain said, "I expected as much."

"The war is almost over, sir," the other sergeant sounded off. "While no one is saying it; the Dutch know it, and we know it."

"Permission to speak freely, sir?" the first sergeant asked.

"Granted," the captain said. "Speak your mind."

"This whole mission is ridiculous, sir. We are just spinning our wheels and wasting time. All to please Captain Wuerff?"

"He's right, sir. Some of our men are complaining. They say, 'We've done our jobs, but we failed to win the war. Why don't we just go on home before any more people have to die?'"

"So that's how they feel, is it?" the captain asked. The sergeants only nodded in rely. "All of them?"

"Yes, sir. That is the general consensus, sir."

At this point in the war, the captain agreed with their sentiments wholeheartedly. He tried to calm his sergeants. He wanted to avoid upsetting the men. "I'll tell you frankly, I've had enough, too. But we're on dangerous ground here. We can't openly quit, not without getting court-martialed. We could still be put in jail, or even face a firing squad."

The first sergeant glanced back at the trucks. The men were sitting perfectly still, uncharacteristically quiet. *We should have moved farther away*, he thought to himself. *They're listening.*

"If you will all give me your word not to betray me or each other, I'll show you a way out.

"Tomorrow, I will report this mission to Captain Wuerff as a failure. The addresses were authentic, and they were most certainly used in the recent past. But they were empty.

"I hope the prisoner who gave up the addresses isn't blamed. He could not have known. In any case, that's his problem now.

"As for me, I am planning to leave this country in a few days. I am going back home.

"As soldiers, you do not have that luxury. But, after I am gone, you will have no one to report to." The captain raised his voice now, so the men could hear. "I suggest that you dress in civilian clothes and make your way home, back to Germany.

"No one is going to report you, so there'll be no one looking for you. Do as I say, go back home and rebuild our country. Drivers, return your trucks to the barracks. Sergeants, do not report in. I will take care of that."

The following morning the captain reported in to Wuerff, "The addresses that the prisoner gave us were authentic, but the Jews were gone. We could find no one at those farms."

Captain Wuerff frowned, and swore under his breath. "Do you have anything else to report then?"

"Captain, most of the Jews in this country have long since reached the destinations that we'd intended for them. Sir, I suggest that we finalize our positions here, burn our records, and be ready to surrender to the Americans."

Wuerff shook his head at this, and growled, "Enough of this talk! I should report you for insubordination . . . and for defeatism . . . and . . . ah, but it matters little now, does it not?

"I know that you have worked well, captain, and you have done your duty. . . ." Wuerff trailed off. "I know that you did all that you could. I thank you for your service to the Fatherland. . . . And I will see you back in Germany, hopefully soon."

Captain Wuerff had made his final plans. A few days before, he'd ordered one more boxcar. He intended to deliver one more train load—including those who had worked against him—to the concentration camp.

Then his work would be done.

CHAPTER THIRTY-ONE

The Platoon Captain

On a brisk spring morning in 1944, three Nazi captains had three unique sets of plans. Each of them no longer served the Third Reich.

The platoon captain had proposed a slowdown of activities. In other words, a strike—an act of pure insubordination. When it occurs during war, it is punishable by death.

He risked not only his own life, but the lives of his men as well. By involving his entire platoon of sixty soldiers, three sergeants, and a sergeant-major, he had put their necks into the noose as well. The platoon captain had foolishly confused an army unit with a labor union. They are not the same. With his strike, he had gambled—a bit too soon—and lost.

Now he would atone for his foolish mistake. The young captain stood at attention before the desk of Captain Wuerff, who had a plan of his own. Wuerff's plan would prove to be of little or no benefit to the Third Reich.

Captain Wuerff was briefed about the latest *razzia* results on the previous day. While the list of addresses had proven to be accurate, it also appeared to have been totally uscless.

Yes, there had been Jews at those locations, but they had left their hiding places. Some had gone only days before the *razzia*, while others had left as long as months before.

"Do you think the prisoners gave us that particular list on purpose?" Wuerff asked.

"Perhaps, but they may not have known that the Jews were gone," the platoon captain replied. "On the other hand, it's possible that they sent us on a wild goose chase. Is there any way we can get the truth out of them?"

"These Resistance men are very tough, they seem to ignore pain." Wuerff shook his head and sighed. "They are very determined to lead us astray.

"I will send some men over to work on them, to vigorously encourage their collaboration." Wuerff gave a cruel smile. "If the prisoners are less than forthcoming, then they may punish them for lack of cooperation. It is of no consequence," he leaned back in his chair and stretched, "they will be transported tonight anyway, before the Americans arrive."

The platoon captain asked a final, loaded question. "What do you expect to happen to us in the next few days?"

Wuerff said nothing, he simply looked quizzically up at him.

"Will you be going along on the next train?" the young captain continued to prod, "and taking your men with you?"

Wuerff merely nodded, "Thank you for your service, captain. You are dismissed. Good luck in the coming days."

TWO INTERROGATORS entered the prison cell and found Kees already standing upright. Battered and bruised, he leaned against the wall, using it to hold himself up. He looked the two tormentors straight in the eyes, and they advanced on him menacingly, determined to make him avert his gaze.

"You know that this war will be over in the next few days," Kees said. "Do you really want to see my suffering in your mind for the rest of your lives?"

The men slowed to a stop, and looked at each other. They looked at Kees again, almost sheepishly, thinking, *This is true. The war is over. Why should we even bother working him over?* Without a word, the two men turned around and left the cell.

They didn't even attempt to enter the next cell, where Frans was waiting for his turn. He knew the Nazis would have found his list useless. That they would have turned up not a single Jew. They were bound to take their disappointment out on him.

But the two interrogators just walked on down the hallway. "I am not going to do this anymore," one man said to the other. "I'm quitting. How about you?"

The other man nodded, "I'm done. This rotten war may end tomorrow. We should lay low and wait it out, so we can go home and live our lives in peace."

WUERFF CALLED his sergeant-major into his office. "I have an important mission for you. Go to the house of Kees van Rijn, you know the address, don't you?"

"That's the one we've been chasing for weeks," the sergeant-major said. "The one that we finally caught?"

"Yes, the same man. Take two men with you. I'd like you to deliver a message to the his wife.

"Let her know that she may visit her husband in the prison, and she may clean him up. She should pack a change of clothes for him, and as much money as she can bring. She may also bring along their son.

"Her visit must take place today. Tomorrow will be too late."

The sergeant-major saluted and left to make arrangements. A short while later, he and his two men arrived at Kees' house. The sergeant-major rang the doorbell, but there was no answer. He knocked on the door, again no answer.

"Break it down," sergeant-major said to one of his troopers. The man kicked the door in, breaking the latch. The sergeant-major pushed it open and walked in.

HARRY AND CORNELIUS were in the backyard of the van Rijn house, where Harry was watching Cornelius in his garden. He was amazed by what the little five-year-old boy had grown on his own. There was an abundance of flowers and vegetables, in productive, tidy little rows. Harry wondered how the little boy had put it all together. It was truly remarkable, and must have been a welcome help in feeding the family during the war.

Harry jumped in surprise when a sergeant and a pair of soldiers suddenly appeared at the back door of the house. The sergeant walked into the yard, looking from side to side appreciatively, taking in all of the greenery.

"Gentlemen, what can I do for you?" Harry asked.

"We are looking for the wife of Kees van Rijn," the sergeant said. "She lives here, does she not?"

"Yes, as a matter of fact, she does. Johanna has gone to visit friends at a farm, but she will be back in a day or two."

"Well, she is allowed to visit her husband in prison," the sergeant-major said, "but only for today."

"Is it possible to contact her? I'm afraid that, by tomorrow, it will be too late. Her husband will be leaving town."

"I will see if I can reach her," Harry said. "Where shall I tell her to go, when I have found her?"

"Her husband is in the prison in Scheveningen; but if she will report to Captain Wuerff at the police station on the Rijswijkse Plein, he will have her taken to the prison to see her husband."

The sergeant-major gave Harry the rest of the instructions, then finished with, "By the way, she may also bring her son. You will remember this?"

"I will remember," Harry replied.

The sergeant saluted politely, and left, the two soldiers right behind him. Harry followed them through the house. One of the men clumsily pulled the broken door closed behind them.

Around the corner, one of the soldiers pulled a bicycle out of the truck, while the other kept watch on the van Rijn house.

"Let's see if he really does go to a farm. Follow him at some distance," the sergeant-major said, "we must remain unnoticed. We'll stay well behind you with the truck.

"Hopefully, the other prisoner's wife is in the same place."

Suddenly Harry burst out from the backyard on his bicycle, with Cornelius on the back. He took off down the road, pedaling furiously. The soldier mounted his bicycle and followed him, keeping enough distance not to be noticed.

The truck followed the soldier at an even greater distance.

"You never know with these Dutch people," the sergeant-major thought aloud, "They're surprisingly clever. In many ways they have been able to outsmart us."

CHAPTER THIRTY-TWO

Trapping Johanna and Cornelius

O ver at Leendert's house, Johanna and Adriana saw Harry roll to a stop. He lifted Cornelius off the bicycle, and together they dashed for the front door. Johanna quickly pulled the door open, and they rushed in.

"Is anything wrong, Harry?" Johanna asked, with a tremor in her voice. She swept Cornelius up in a hug.

"Yes and no," Harry said, "I have some really good news, I think; but I don't know if we should trust this situation."

Leendert came to the room and said, "Harry, tell us exactly what happened."

"Okay, we were in the backyard, and I was admiring Cornelius' garden, when three Nazis broke into the house!

"A sergeant told me that the Germans were giving you a one-time chance to visit Kees. But it can only be today. Tomorrow they are transporting Kees out of the city.

"You can clean him up, bring him a fresh set of clothes, and as much money as you can get."

"That last bit makes the whole story stink," Leendert said. "Did they follow you here, Harry?"

"I don't think so. Cornelius, why don't you go outside and pretend to play. Then wander down the street and see if there any Nazis or trucks waiting there?"

It was one of those chores that Cornelius loved, playing a spy. He had done it many times before, and he was good at it. After all, who would suspect a little boy?

Cornelius came back in several minutes later, very excited. He said to Leendert, "There is a truck on the next corner, and one soldier right across the street.

"When I came out of the front door, he looked at me, and followed me. But I stopped and played for a minute with my friend three houses down. So he turned back around and waited at the same spot as before."

"That's good work, Cornelius," Leendert said. "Harry, that means they followed you here. I wonder why?

"You should go out to the truck, Harry, and see if they're the same men who came to Kees' house. Ask them why they've followed you. Tell them that you did your job, and that you've told Johanna she can visit Kees in prison."

"Okay," Harry said, "I'll do it."

Johanna looked worried. "I hope I'm doing the right thing, going to the prison," she said. "I guess I have to trust my instincts.

"I know I need to see my husband. Who knows what they've done to him? If I don't go now, who knows if I'll ever see him again?" She sat down and took Cornelius on her lap.

"What do you think, son? Should we go and visit daddy in the prison?"

Cornelius nodded his head, "Yes, mom. We should."

"Good boy. I think we might bring him some hope if we do. I sure want to see him."

Johanna was both saddened and proud. Cornelius, her smart little boy, had learned so much during the worst possible times that a child could ever have.

Harry returned through the front door. "Yes, these are the same soldiers. They said that they wanted to make sure I brought their message to you.

"The sergeant reminded me that Kees needs fresh clothes. He also said that he leaves tomorrow, but he may be back soon, because the Americans are coming any day now. It seems that they too are expecting the war to end very soon."

"Since you've been the messenger, and the Nazis know you, Harry," Leendert said, "why don't you take Johanna and Cornelius back home? After they get the clothes, you can escort them to the police station, so they can visit Kees as soon as possible."

Johanna, Cornelius, and Harry said their goodbyes, and they began the walk home. Out on the street, Johanna carried Cornelius, while Harry walked his bicycle. At a discreet distance, the truck slowly followed them to their home.

It was growing dark when they finally arrived at the former police station. The sergeant on duty said, "Hello. We've been waiting for you. Captain Wuerff had me arrange a car for you. Your driver will be here soon, if you'll wait a few minutes.

"Did you bring the things you were told to bring?"

Johanna nodded, then turned to Harry. "Thank you so much for helping us. You may as well go. We'll be visiting Kees soon. Then, we'll come back to your house."

CHAPTER THIRTY-THREE

The General Packs Up

It was the middle of April, and it had been raining all day long. General Habsberger had been waiting for a break in the weather, but it seemed as if one would never come. The preparations to depart had all been made. Everyone was finally ready for the big move. But if the rain continued, the operation would have to be postponed.

It wasn't until nearly ten o'clock that evening that the rain finally slowed. By the top of the hour, it had stopped. The General jumped into his car and raced across rain-slick roads to the former ambassador's villa in Wassenaar.

The sergeant-major had been watching the weather as well. When he saw the General's car pull in through the driveway, he bellowed an order to the soldiers, who were now dressed in civilian clothing. "The General is here. Start the loading!"

The General heard the command as well and chided the sergeant, "Stop behaving like you're military. Remember what I had said? You're civilians now."

"Yes, sir," the sergeant-major said. The General sighed, old habits were indeed hard to break. The sergeant waved Haagendoorn over, he then politely asked the curator to inform the former soldiers which items should be loaded first. The General gave a half smile, perhaps old dogs could learn new tricks.

"Be very careful," Haagendoorn urged, "each box, each package, each cylinder represents your future." The truck was loaded quietly and efficiently.

As the men worked, he took a final look around the confiscated villa, to see if anything had been overlooked. His eye fell on an antique English grandfather clock.

He called two of the men over to take the clock, and asked them to pack it on top of the boxes in the truck. As they hauled it away, he said, "Okay, let's go. We meet the submarine at one hour after midnight."

The General and the sergeant-major climbed into the old Mercedes Cabriolet, and pulled away, taking the lead before the two large trucks. The lead truck hauled away the looted treasure, while the trailing truck carried Haagendoorn and all of the men.

Just after midnight, the convoy pulled to a stop at the fishermen's harbor of Katwijk. The truck with the booty backed up to about ten yards from the entrance to the pier. A fishing boat was tied up alongside.

Silently, the men began to unload the boxes and crates. They carried them onto the pier and handed them down into the boat. In short order, the entire load was stacked deep in the hold of the fishing boat, where mountains of caught fish were usually stored.

Even though the hold had been otherwise empty, the smell of fish was still very potent. Some of the men, those not used to the sea, could not help but gag at the powerful odor.

Suddenly, the pier was lit up by the headlights of what must have been a dozen trucks. No one had heard them coming, so they may have been there all along. Then, through a loudspeaker, a German voice demanded, "*Haende hoch, jedermann* (Hands-up, everyone). Come out in front of the trucks, so we can see you. If you have guns, drop them. Anyone who's caught hiding a weapon will be shot."

A young captain stepped forward, backed up by several dozen troops. He waved a signal, and the soldiers spread out among the men in civilian clothes. Guns in hand, the troops at the perimeter maintained watch, while others moved throughout the group placing handcuffs on the men. The "civilians" remained completely silent. They remembered the General's advice, "Do not say a word. You're supposed to be Dutchmen."

As the young platoon captain came closer, General Habsberger stepped towards him and demanded in perfect German, "Identify yourself, captain. Who has sent you? And why are you interfering with this most-secret mission of the Reich?"

Momentarily flustered, the platoon captain said not a word. The General repeated his demand, loudly. The captain opened his mouth to reply, then closed it again.

The General took a step forward and leaned in close to the captain. In a low voice, he spoke a single sentence, one which the others were unable to hear.

At the implied threat, the armed soldiers closed in on the General and lowered their guns at him.

In a low voice, the captain softly repeated the single sentence that General Habsberger had spoken. He seemed lost in thought.

The General nodded silently at him.

The captain straightened, took one step back, and shouted out a command. "Release them, and retreat!" The soldiers removed the handcuffs from the men in Dutch civilian clothes. Then, they turned around, retreated through the group, and disappeared back into the trucks. The dozen pairs of headlights switched off in ragged fashion, and the pier was once again shrouded in darkness and silence.

The General shook hands with the platoon captain, who stepped back and saluted. The General just tipped his hat. Without another word the captain disappeared into the dark as well. With no further commands, the dozen trucks fired up loudly and retreated into the darkness. In minutes, silence blanketed the entire harbor area once more.

The General looked at his watch as he walked over to the fisherman. "We'll have to wait another ten minutes," he softly said. "One more passenger will be joining us. As soon as you see him coming, start engines and we'll get out of the harbor."

No one recognized the man in civilian clothes, who emerged from the darkness eight minutes later. As he boarded the boat, some of the men were surprised to see the platoon captain who had commanded the trucks. He too was leaving the men under his command without their leader.

The fishing boat slowly backed away from the dock, then turned towards the mouth of the harbor. The two empty trucks and the Mercedes remained abandoned on the dock.

Once it had cleared the harbor, the engine of the fishing boat cranked up to full speed. The bow began to kick up spray. Their destination was the middle of the ocean, a pre-planned coordinate in the North Sea.

The fisherman kept close track of the time on his watch. He calculated that it would take exactly 45 minutes to join up with the submarine. He had the men keep watch for the signal light that would tell them where the submarine waited.

The men down below decks were silent, a few were seasick. Occasionally someone whispered something, and a quiet laugh helped to break the tension. The men were used to taking action, they needed something to do. Waiting was difficult.

The fishing-boat captain, and his crew of two men, had also changed into their civilian clothes. They anxiously checked their watches, certain that they were getting close.

The submarine was already there, lurking just below the surface at periscope depth. On the hydrophones, the crew listened as the fishing boat approached.

At 12:45 a.m., the submarine commander raised a hand, and said softly, "Time to surface." An alarm sounded, followed by the roar of rushing air and water. A lookout spun open the hatch, and practically leapt out of the sub to take up his position. In seconds, several sailors were scanning the surface and sky for targets. A moment later, they spied the fishing boat less than half a mile to the east. One of the crew flashed a signal light three times.

The fisherman did the same and adjusted his course fifteen degrees to the north. The boat turned toward the sub. He was pleased that his calculations had proven accurate. He smiled at the General, who nodded in approval.

Habsberger turned to face his crew of former soldiers, and said, "Be ready to move, gentlemen. The time has come to transfer our valuable cargo onto the ship. The ship that will bring us our freedom."

The sea was calm, with long swells that gently lifted the boat as it slowly closed with the sub. A row of old tires hung along the sides of the trawler. Ropes were tossed across and the two vessels were tied together. The trawler crew used boat hooks to fend the trawler off from the sub.

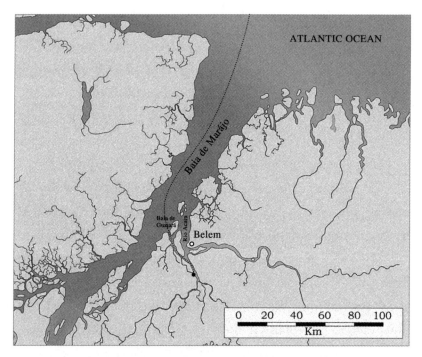

The route of the German submarine into the jungles of the Amazon and to its dugout up the Rio Acara.

The submarine was close aboard now, but not close enough to allow the men to jump across. Ropes were used to pull a large fishing net across the gap. It was then spread open between the boat and the sub, to prevent any of their precious cargo from falling into the sea.

The trawler crew used the boom of the fishing boat to transfer a number of men onto the submarine first. Then, the sailors moved the boom back and forth, hauling the crates and other cargo from the hold of the fishing boat across to the submarine. Sailors shouted commands and men pulled at the lines. It was dangerous work, but it was smoothly and efficiently done. In just over an hour the crates and cargo had been moved across and stowed below.

The trawler captain was the last man to transfer over to the submarine. He and his crewmen untied the ropes and the fishing nets themselves. With some reluctance, the captain let go of the last rope. "She wasn't much," he said, "but she was mine." The trawler eventually floated back to the Netherlands with the tide, where it washed up on the beach.

Rather than submerge again, the submarine stayed on the surface at night, where it could run at high speed to cover more distance. Blacked out and under radio silence, the helmsman steered the sub north-northeast to sail out of the North Sea.

The sub rounded Scotland, passed south of Iceland, then entered the Atlantic Ocean. The captain charted a course well away from the shores of Canada and the United States, and their sub-hunting bombers. During the day, lookouts searched intently for Allied ships and planes of their hunter-killer groups. The war was not over yet.

Their final destination was the city of Belem, in Brazil, and the mouth of the Amazon. It would be a shame to be caught this close to the end.

CHAPTER THIRTY-FOUR

Johanna Visits Her Husband

Johanna had taken a little suitcase with the suit that Kees liked to wear on Sundays. A fresh, clean white shirt, a few pairs of socks, and some underwear were packed neatly. She began to grow very anxious as she and Cornelius approached the single cell where Kees had been kept.

The soldier opened the door for her, and together with her son they walked in. What Johanna saw made her burst into tears. She tried to choke them back. When Cornelius saw his father, he too began to cry. Through his tears, he said, "Daddy, daddy, what have they done to you? Can you still stand?"

Kees was lying on the floor, bloodied, battered, and crumpled up like an old rag doll. Johanna braced herself and tried to lift him up by the arms, but he could not stand up.

The only chair in the room was bloodied as well, but she pulled it closer. After a great deal of effort, Johanna and Cornelius got Kees to sit on the chair. She could see that he was in terrible pain, it was written all over his face. Great bruises and stripes of blood marred his good looks and had stained all his clothes. Johanna barely knew where to start.

"I need water," she said. "Cornelius ask the soldier outside to bring us some water in a bucket or a bowl. It doesn't matter how, but without water I cannot clean him up."

Outside the cell door, a soldier was keeping watch over the cell. When he saw Cornelius approach the door, he opened the little window and asked, "What do you want?"

Cornelius stopped, puzzled. "I don't know what he's saying, mom. Can you come to the door and ask him?"

A few minutes later, the soldier returned with a large bowl filled with cold water. Fortunately, Johanna had brought along soap and towels. Carefully she began washing her husband's face, and he smiled painfully. "Thank you," he whispered.

"Cornelius, give me a hand. We will have to take these filthy clothes off of your dad. Everything must hurt him now, so be as careful as you can. If necessary, we can tear the clothes—they're ruined anyway."

Together, the pair of them worked gently for what seemed like hours. The dried blood was carefully washed away, and the more severe wounds were bandaged. Finally Kees began to look a little bit better. Johanna helped Kees to stand, while Cornelius helped him put on his clean shirt and pants.

With a painful smile on his face, he said, "Now, a nice steak dinner and I'll be back in shape to face my tormentors."

"Thank God, you haven't lost your sense of humor," Johanna said, smiling sadly. Her heart was breaking for him.

Cornelius looked at his dad in awe. "How did you survive this, dad?"

Kees shook his head and said, "I couldn't begin to tell you, but somehow God gave me the strength, son. Without Him, I would have given in to their demands long ago, and then I would simply have died." He sighed heavily, and the gave a small smile. "But I think the ordeal is almost over now, and I hope they'll let me go home soon."

Johanna knocked at the cell door, and the soldier standing guard pulled it open in an instant. Three more soldiers now stood behind the man who had opened the door. "Can we go now?" Johanna said, "My husband is all cleaned up, but he's in no condition for a long walk. We'll need a truck to take us home."

"Yes, the truck will be here soon," the soldier said. "Just wait until we come to pick you up."

He closed the door behind him, and they walked away. He flashed a cruel smile at the other men, "They think they're going home. I think they're in for a surprise."

CHAPTER THIRTY-FIVE

The N.S.B.

T he *Nationale Socialistische Beweging Nederland* (National Socialistic Movement of the Netherlands) was a political party founded by a Dutchman, Anton Mussert, in 1931. His party program contained language similar to that which was used by the German national socialist party, the Nazis. However, it did not mention anything about the Jews.

In 1936, the NSB party had more than 52,000 members in the Netherlands and it was fast growing in popularity. The party managed to get eight members elected to the Dutch parliament, and they were even supported by the Roman Catholic Church. Eventually, anti-Jewish extremists in the party forced it to adopt the anti-semitic attitudes of the Nazis, and the membership began to decline.

With the German invasion, membership began to increase, as some citizens chose to back what they saw as the strong horse in the race. By 1944, the membership would reach 100,000. The party leader, Mussert, was not appointed to be the prime minister of the country, as he'd hoped the Nazis would do. Instead, he was given the job of controlling the public's resistance to the Ger-

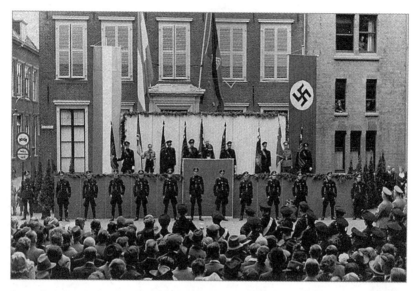

A meeting of the NSB (*Nationale Socialistische Beweging Nederland*) in Utrecht, 1941. A Dutch version of the Nazi party had as many as 52,000 members five years before the war began. It doubled in size during the war.

man occupation of the country. As a result, he worked together with the Gestapo to collect the more uncooperative Dutch citizens. These "troublemakers" quickly found their way to concentration camps in Germany and Poland.

Mussert also oversaw the creation of an all-volunteer Dutch SS panzergrenadier division, to contribute to the German war effort. He appealed again to Berlin for a greater role, so Adolf Hitler named him as *Leider van het Nederlandse Volk* (Leader of the Dutch People). It was, however, a ceremonial role, with no real power. Hitler had installed a devout Nazi in the position of *Reichskommissar* (National Commissioner) for Holland, and that was where the real power was. It would remain that way for the rest of the German occupation.

Arthur Seyss-Inquart had been appointed governor of the Ostmark, or Austria, which had been annexed by Germany. As soon as he took office, Seyss-Inquart confiscated all Jewish property and commenced sending the Jews to concentration camps. With the surrender of the Netherlands, he was appointed *Reichskommissar* and he continued his anti-Jewish policies in Holland, doing his best to make sure that every Dutch Jew was sent to the camps. He was terribly efficient at his work. Of the 140,000 Jews registered by the Jewish Council in Holland, only 30,000 would survive the war.

At the end of the war in Europe, Seyss-Inquart was captured crossing an Elbe River bridge by a pair of Royal Welch Fusiliers, one of whom was an escaped German Jew. Norbert Mueller had escaped to Britain at age 15, just before the war began. He had returned as part of the British Army. His entire family had died in the concentration camps.

Seyss-Inquart was tried and convicted at the Nuremberg war crimes trials and received the sentence of death. Some of his last words were, "Death by hanging . . . well, in view of the whole situation, I never expected anything different." He was hanged in October of 1946.

Most leaders of the NSB were similarly arrested and tried. Many were sentenced to long jail sentences. Anton Mussert was sentenced to death and faced the firing squad, poetically, on the Waalsdorpervlakte dunes, where the hundreds of Resistance men had been executed.

After the war, and the subsequent war crimes trials, the former Resistance men joked that NSB stood for *Niet So Bedoeld* (not so intended), or "I didn't mean it."

CHAPTER THIRTY-SIX

The Stables at Van Gend & Loos

For three days, the seventy-two Jews from Barneveld had survived in the Van Gend & Loos stables on little or no food. If they were lucky, they received a single cup of watery soup each day. There was also a water barrel, but the Germans could not be bothered to supply a dipper. They had to scoop the water with their hands in order to drink any.

Everyone sat on the straw-covered floor, with their little suitcases next to them. Many tried to gather some of the straw for use as a makeshift bed. Whatever clothes they had, they used as a pillow.

People sat in little groups, giving each other hope that the war would end before they were loaded onto one of the trains. Since they had arrived, not one of the soldiers had come back to the holding cell. Perhaps the Americans would come in time.

The people that had already been there before they arrived said that they would be boarding the next day. As each day passed without incident, they grew certain that it would happen on the next one. The weary, starving people were growing very discouraged about their hopeless situation.

Feeling some responsibility for their former guests, the two farmers and their wives had taken charge.

Krelis, the chicken farmer, made a suggestion. "I'll go to the door and knock until someone opens up. Then, I'll demand to speak to the commander of this unit.

"They must help us with some food, at least. Maybe we can get an answer about what will to happen to us."

He crossed to the door and began banging relentlessly. He kept at it for two hours, until finally an annoyed soldier unlocked and opened the door. Behind him were a dozen more men with guns at the ready, just in case anyone tried to escape. Krelis made his demand but the soldier at the door merely shook his head and closed it again.

This only made Krelis even angrier, and he began pounding on the door once again. After a minute or two of the booming noise, several shots rang out and the farmer crumpled to the ground. The soldiers had shot several rounds right through the door, killing the man instantly. Nobody dared to move towards the man for fear of being shot as well.

Hours later, a squad of soldiers entered the hall. The men fanned out, rifles lowered at the crowd, and the squad leader stepped forward. He selected five women out of the crowd. "You will come with us," the squad leader said. "The captain in charge wishes to speak with you. Afterwards, you may relate what he tells you to the people here."

The women were led into a former Van Gend & Loos executive office. The soldiers closed and locked the door behind them without a word. The women were left to wait in fear.

Fifteen minutes later, Captain Wuerff entered the room. He said to them, "*Entshuldigen, meine damen* (sorry, ladies), but we have no food for you tonight. However, you will soon board the train for your final destination."

The women tried to ask questions, but the Captain turned around abruptly and left through the door. The soldiers then re-entered the office and escorted the women back to the stable. As soon as the Germans had gone, they were surrounded by their fellow refugees and bombarded with questions.

One of the ladies raised her hands to quiet the crowd. Once they had settled down, she spoke. "The only thing that the captain said is that there is no food for tonight, and that we will be going on the train soon to our final destination."

This was not the news that they had hoped for.

CHAPTER THIRTY-SEVEN

Loading the Last Train

T hree sergeants and one sergeant-major stood rigidly at attention before Captain Wuerff, at the old police station on the Rijswijkse Plein in The Hague.

"Gentlemen, today marks the beginning of the end of your time in the army. One more mission, then you will all have your freedom." One of the sergeants cracked a smile at the news.

"You will each select twelve men to join us on the train. We begin loading at 22:00 hours tonight. I want you all to be at the station an hour before we begin.

"I have prepared a passenger carriage for you, so pack your belongings and order your men to do the same. We will not be coming back."

The sergeants glanced at each other, trying to suppress their excitement. Germany? They were going home!

"I have ordered one boxcar for the Jewish prisoners," Wuerff continued. "It will be a tight fit, but they deserve no better."

"You will have your men report to the station with their weapons loaded. I do not want any surprises. If anyone gives you trouble, you have permission to shoot them."

189

Now the men glanced at each other in mild concern. Was the Captain expecting some kind of trouble? If so, they would be ready.

"I have ensured that there will be no one else at the station," Wuerff said. "The freight elevators are no longer in operation. When we move the prisoners, you will station one squad down in the stables and another up in the station. The rest of the men you will distribute along the stairways, within sight of each other. There will be no escapes. If anyone tries, shoot them."

"Sir, you said that we won't be coming back," the sergeant-major said. "Does that mean we may go home after we've delivered these people?"

"Yes, those are my intentions," Wuerff said. "It depends on what we find at the camp. Theoretically, they will have no use for you there. So as far as I'm concerned, at that point you are discharged and dismissed."

Wuerff sent the sergeants away to do their duty; but asked the sergeant-major to remain behind a moment. "I have an assignment for you, one that needs to be carefully conducted.

"At the jail in Scheveningen, there are four people: two men, a woman, and a boy. They will need to be picked up and brought directly to the station.

"I do not want them there any earlier than 23:00 hours, and I want you to make sure that all loading has been completed before they arrive. They are to be our final guests. As soon as they are in, close the doors, and we will depart."

The sergeant-major confirmed the assignment, snapped his boots together at attention, then turned on his heel and left.

The Captain had already packed his belongings. Four suitcases sat just inside his office door. The night before, he had gathered the pictures of his wife and children, his special hand guns, his trophies, and the spoils he had plundered from the homes of Jews he had arrested. The suitcases were packed tight.

At the proper hour, his driver came up to the office to carry his suitcases down to the car. They were heavy enough that the man ordered an aide to help. Once they were packed into the trunk, they left for the Van Gend & Loos stables.

As they drove, the Captain leaned forward to thank his faithful driver. "Wilfred, after you have dropped me off, you are free to go. You are dismissed."

The drivers eyebrows raised at that. Dismissed for the day? Or dismissed for good? He waited for the Captain to elaborate.

"You may use the car. It is the property of the Reich, but you may use it as long as you can get away with it. As far as I am concerned, you can go back to Germany."

The driver smiled now. This was getting better and better.

"You are dismissed from your service under me. I hope you can return home safely as a good German citizen."

Wilfred was elated, for him the war had come to an end. He pulled into the Van Gend & Loos stables, and unloaded the suitcases. He set them down carefully next to a guard—they were be this man's problem now. Then Wilfred shook the Captain's hand and drove away.

Wuerff walked into the stables and began shouting orders. He pointed to a pair of guards, "You, and you. Take my suitcases up to the passenger car on the platform." The guards grabbed the cases, and struggled under their weight as they climbed the stairs. One of them swore about the broken freight elevator.

The sergeants had their men already in place, ready to move the Jewish prisoners from the stables up to the station.

"Bring all your belongings," Wuerff shouted. "Leave nothing behind because you will not be coming back. The train is waiting for you, the soldiers will lead you until you're safely aboard."

Like sheep brought to the slaughter, the two-hundred prisoners walked up the stairs in silence and in fear. They crossed the platform and lined up before the cattle car.

"Leave your baggage here," the soldiers ordered. "There won't be room enough in this car. We'll load it into the first car for safekeeping."

As the soldiers prodded the crowd into the car, some families were separated. One woman cried, "Please, I want to stay with my husband and child." The soldiers simply ignored her plea, and any like it.

Once the first hundred people had boarded, the remaining people on the platform began to voice their fears. "Isn't there a second train wagon? How are we all going to fit in there?" Again, the soldiers ignored their remarks and began to push people into the cattle car.

The noise became louder as the people were crushed together or against the walls of the car. They cried out, "We can't do this! We won't fit! How long are we going to be in here?"

Others were adapting to their predicament, and voiced questions like, "How long will the trip be? Will we stop for toilet breaks? Can we have some water?"

With no answers forthcoming, the questions and cries only grew, becoming louder and louder. Finally, the last prisoner was shoved inside, the big door rolled closed, and the lock was latched into place.

The screaming and crying continued inside, but no one was there to hear. The soldiers had all walked away, unwilling to lis-

Two hundred people were pressed together in this cattle car. There was no room to move or to sit, no food or drink, and no place to go to the bathroom.

ten any longer. The train did not move, it simply sat there with the locomotive idling and occasionally blowing off excess steam. For a long time the train sat waiting at the station, waiting for Wuerff's special delivery from the jail.

A SPECIAL TRUCK had arrived at the Orange Hotel. It did not go in through the main entrance of the jail. Instead, it parked in front of the small black door that opened nearby. This was the door through which so many had been taken, to meet the firing squad at the Waalsdorpervlakte dunes.

The four people who climbed into the truck were unaware of that particular use of the door. They had great hopes. Finally, they were going home. To them, the door meant freedom.

Frans had not seen his wife for weeks. He still looked battered and bruised, so Johanna used the damp cloth that she had to try to clean up his face. "Anna will be so happy to see you," she said. "We must try to make you at least a little presentable."

Cornelius grasped his father's hand. "Are you going to stay at home with us now, dad? Mom and I were so scared when you didn't come back. My friends say that the war is over now."

Kees nodded his head, and while looking at Johanna, he said, "Yes, son. I will be staying home. Unfortunately, the war is not really over yet. We'll have to be very careful in what we say, or do, because the soldiers may come to our house again."

Kees changed the subject. "How is your garden doing, son?"

"We're starting to pick the first strawberries now," Cornelius said proudly.

"That's great. Did you plant new potatoes last week?"

"I started them from peels and they're planted in a box."

"I wonder how your marigolds are doing," Kees said, "they should have started to bloom by now."

Cornelius was proud of his garden, he beamed whenever his father showed interest in his work. "Yes, dad. Everything I wanted to do is done, and the marigolds have buds already.

"When we get home, I need to get some water from the river and water all of my plants. I haven't been able to do that while you were gone."

The truck slowed down; but with the canvas closed, no one could see where they were. When one of the soldiers opened the back of the truck they found themselves looking at the railway station in The Hague.

Kees asked, "Where are we going? This is nowhere near our home, and we can't walk all the way from here."

The soldier shook his head. "You are not going home. You are all going on the train."

"But where is it going?" Johanna asked desperately. "I haven't brought anything! How long will we be on the train?"

"I should have known," Frans muttered. Kees nodded sadly. Without another word, the soldiers pushed the four up the stairs and towards the train platform. Their weapons were held plainly in view—there would be no complaining tolerated.

Kees saw that a short train rested on the tracks—a locomotive, a passenger car, and a single boxcar. A small group of soldiers stood near the door of the boxcar; as they approached, one of the men unlatched it and pulled open the door.

They were horrified at what they saw. The boxcar was packed full of people. Far worse than a can of sardines, it seemed there was not an inch of room for even one more person. Yet, into it they would go, whether they liked it or not. The soldiers pushed hard against the people, wedged the four of them in, and closed the door behind them.

Johanna was crying, and Cornelius could hardly look up, it was so tight. He couldn't move or even raise his hands, it was so tight that he began to scream.

"I don't want to go on the train, daddy! Let's get out!"

Kees didn't answer, because there was nothing to say. Uncle Frans said not a word either. His mother continued to cry, and Cornelius began to cry too. The rest of the people were silent, they understood. They were all cried out, and had come to terms with their terrible situation.

Suddenly, the train began to move, and the boxcar rattled and shook its way down the tracks, jostling the people against each other. The people realized that standing tight together was not so terrible—for the time being. At least it kept them from falling down. The train slowed down, then speeded up again, many times. Crushed together in the dark as they all were, they lost any sense of time. The train ride seemed to go on forever, and they wondered where it would end.

After a long four hours that only seemed like an eternity, the train stopped abruptly. Among the crowd, hope quickly rose that they had reached their destination. At least, they would be allowed out of the boxcar.

But the door was never opened. The train did not move. And their spirits began to fall.

No one had any idea how long they waited. It was impossible to raise an arm to look at a watch. No one knew the distance they had traveled, or how long it would take to reach their destination.

The train did not move for a long time. Eventually, it began to roll again, but slower this time.

IN THE PASSENGER CAR of the train, the soldiers and their leaders were having a good time. Stops and starts did not concern them. Neither did long waits.

Wuerff had made sure that his men would be comfortable. He'd brought along a great store of liquor, beer, and food, all "requisitioned" from the army commissaries or confiscated from bootleggers and black marketeers.

The troops were relaxed, and happily enjoying themselves. The men had great hopes that, upon arrival in the concentration camp, they would be able to go home to their families.

Suddenly the train slowed to a stop again. Captain Wuerff wondered at the delay—he was still eager to finish his mission.

He sent a sergeant up to the locomotive to discover why the train to come to a stop.

The soldier returned a few minutes later and asked Wuerff to go with him. "There is a group of soldiers and an officer blocking the way," the soldier said. "They tell us that we cannot go any farther. The Westerbork concentration camp has supposedly been closed."

They walked together to the front of the train, and Wuerff's anger grew with every step. He approached the officer who led the blockade, and demanded an answer. "Why wasn't I told about this before I left The Hague? How am I going to get this train turned around?"

"You should have checked with dispatch yourself, sir," the blockading officer said reproachfully. "You should also know by now that camps are closing all across the Reich."

Captain Wuerff swore vehemently. Then he took a moment to regain his composure. "Tell me then, how are we to proceed from here?"

"You can turn your train around at 10:00 tomorrow morning. We will arrange to clear a track for you to do so, at the station in Zwolle. Until then, I am sorry, but you will have to stay here for the rest of the night."

The victims in the cattle car were filled with hope. Many asked, "Have we arrived already? Where could we be?"

One man guessed that they had been on the rails for about four hours. That meant that they were probably still in the Netherlands. But if so, where could that be?

Some of them had ideas. "I think we're in Eindhoven," one man suggested. "Or maybe Nijmegen," said another.

"No, those will be too close to the Americans."

"It must be Arnhem then," said another man. "I sure hope the Allies get here soon."

"I think we've gone the other way. I'll bet we're close to Zwolle. But I can't imagine why they would bring us here. Let's hope that they will unload us, at least for a little while."

Time passed, and then more time passed. But the doors never opened.

Some of the people heard soldiers talking just outside the boxcar, but they had no way to speak to them, or ask questions. They began banging on the wooden walls of the car and shouting noisily, but no one reacted to their calls. After a while, the uncaring soldiers simply walked away.

It was no longer their problem. They would be going home very soon.

The Most Horrifying Trip Ever

The trip took four days and four nights to complete. There was no food, no water, and no toilet.

The noises of the people, muffled by the sound of the train on the track, were unbearable and indescribable. Some prayed aloud, others were crying, and some were cursing the Nazis and God. Others were, amazingly, lifting their voices in song, defying death even in the very face of it.

The people were slowly starving, and suffering from dehydration. They were completely exhausted, but unable to sit or lie down. Illnesses were breaking out, and some of the sick threw up in the shoulder-to-shoulder crowd. After so many hours standing in confinement, defecating and urinating were inevitable and unavoidable.

Some people gave up hope of ever reaching a destination at all. They no longer believed that they would be able to survive this horrible, inhuman treatment and return to the world to live a normal life.

By the end, thirty dead bodies were still standing upright, slumped in between the living. They had simply lost their will to live, surrendered to their miserable circumstances, and died on their feet. Screams of pain and agony could be constantly heard during their many hours of miserable transport. And always in the background could be heard the constant wail and moan of the crying and suffering people.

The train stopped many times, and the sounds of shooting, sounds of war could be heard all around them. Then, the train began to move once again.

IN THE PASSENGER CARRIAGE, Captain Wuerff enjoyed his own secluded compartment. Next to it was a second compartment, where the suitcases of the victims had actually been stored.

During the night, Wuerff systematically opened every suitcase, searched them, and removed anything of value that they contained. Money, jewelry, watches, and diamonds were transferred to a trunk that belonged to Captain Wuerff. Once he had looted all of the cases of their valuables, he lugged his trunk back to his compartment.

At the other end of the passenger car, his men were sleeping soundly after their day of celebration and intoxication. They never heard a thing.

THE FOLLOWING PAGES represent the unending and unendurable misery of this terrible trip. Please pause to reflect upon what happened to normal human beings—people no different than you and me—on their way to their deaths.

Too many of us.

Can't breathe.

Howlong is this going to take?

Can't move.

I can't sleep this way.

I am thirsty.

My whole body is hurting.

I can't hold it any longer, ohhh.

Crying.

If they would just stop for a bathroom break.

They are stopping.

Singing the Unetaneh Tokef.

Who will live and who will die?

Anyone join me:

Who by strangling and who by stoning?

How can the Nazis do this to us?

We are stopping here for at least five hours.

What a cruel treatment.

Crying, cursing, singing.

Where are we?

I can't bear this any longer.

We're moving again.

Sorry, I am choking from the smell in here.

Singing. Suffocating noise. Crying. Screaming.

We are moving again.

Let's sing the Unetaneh Tokef once more.

Who will live and who will die?

Who in their time and who not in their time?

DAY FOUR

Join me in the Unetaneh Tokef. . . .

Who by fire and who by beast?

Who will be made humble and who will be raised up?

Who will be calm and who will be tormented?

But teshuvah and tefillah and tzedikah

It is deadly silent in here.

Is everyone still alive?

It is still night.

We're slowing down.

Finally arriving?

THE POEM "UNETANEH TOKEF"

I (DAVID A.M. WILENSKY)

On the High Holidays, we read a poem known by its first two words in Hebrew: *Unetaneh Tokef* (Let Us Cede Power). It was written about a thousand years ago by an unknown author in Northern Europe. Whether one comes to synagogue in order to hear it, or stays away in order not to, the poem epitomizes the High Holiday prayer services for many contemporary Jews. In particular, this compelling and troubling passage from the middle of the poem looms large: On Rosh Hashanah it is written, and on Yom Kippur it is sealed.

How many will pass and how many will be created?

Who will live and who will die?

Who in their time, and who not their time?

Who by fire and who by water?

Who by sword and who by beast?

Who by hunger and who by thirst?

Who by earthquake and who by drowning?

Who by strangling and who by stoning?

Who will rest and who will wander?

Who will be safe and who will be torn?

Who will be calm and who will be tormented?

Who will become poor and who will get rich?

Who will be made humble and who will be raised up?

But teshuvah and tefillah and tzedakah
(*return and prayer and righteous acts*)

Deflect the evil of the decree.

A Glorious Arrival

I t was April 20, 1945, and after six tense days and six long nights, the submarine safely reached the waters of northern Brazil. While there had been several close calls, the bombers of the American hunter-killers groups had never made contact with them.

The commander of the submarine had taken the boat down to Brazil several months before, to scout out the territory. Now that they knew the route, he confidently maneuvered the sub through the great Marájo Bay and into the smaller bay of Guajara. The deep blue of the ocean slowly turned to green as they traveled upstream. The submarine was careful to avoid the city of Belem, which could be seen in the distance.

They followed a course through the middle of the small bay, keeping a close watch on the depth meter. They sailed through the bay, and the water went from green to brown as they approached the mouth of the Acará River.

The submarine slowed to a three-knot crawl, as they passed from the Guajara and headed up into the Rio Acará. The captain and the lookouts scanned the river head, as they carefully avoided approaching sand banks and little islets. They had only ten kilometers more to travel. Running aground now, so near to the end, would be disastrous.

Finally, the submarine reached the end of its voyage. A specially built dugout had been hacked from the shore. This would be the sub's final resting place. Slowly, carefully, it moved into the crude berth.

At the blast from its horn, dozens of Brazilian men appeared out of the woods. In half an hour, the unloading of the precious cargo had begun. The crates and other cargo were stacked well back from the shore, safe on dry land.

For days before the arrival of the submarine, these men had been hard at work, hacking a passageway out of the jungle. The path led deep into the overgrown interior.

It was a very long track, a hike of more than four hours, to the hidden Nazi compound. There would be no trucks on this little excursion. With long poles and big canvas slings, the men took up the cargo, and took on their second role, as porters.

When they finally reached the newly-built compound, everyone was soaked with sweat. The General's wife and children had prepared a huge welcome buffet for them, and they greeted the former soldiers and sailors with cool drinks. The staff had prepared a great variety of tantalizing Brazilian dishes, and their mouths watered at the sight and smells. The new arrivals quickly blended in with the welcoming crowd and a band began to play the German national anthem.

While the Germans relaxed, Haagendoorn directed the porters to a specially-built storage hall. The building was solid and secure; but best of all, it was air-conditioned, to protect the valuable pieces of art. The crates were spread about the storage room and the porters immediately set to work unpacking them. As each piece was revealed, Haagendoorn had them carefully placed onto specially-crafted shelves and storage racks. Once they had finished, the porters were paid and dismissed. There was still work to do, before the art and treasure could be displayed in the gallery, but that would be performed by a crew with a completely different skill set. Teun Haagendoorn planned to create a literal fine art museum in the middle of the jungle.

Each piece of art would have its own unique display, to highlight its particular beauty. The galleries would not be open to just anyone, instead the possible buyers would arrive by special invitation only. They would be welcomed with lavish accommodations, encouraging them to pay the ultimate prices for their treasures.

The Brazilian landowners—whose services General Habsberger had bought with the first of the paintings—had spared no expense to build the spacious compound. Sixty homes surrounded the main house as a castle wall. Cameras were placed along the outer walls, and hundreds of spotlights could light up the surrounding terrain for a hundred meters beyond the buildings. Nothing, or no one, could penetrate the settlement without being seen.

The submarine commander had sated himself with the delicious Brazilian food, washing it down with uncounted glasses of Caipirinha, a cocktail of sugarcane liquor and lime. He had forgotten all about his submarine, which rested in the little inlet of the Rio Acará. The commander owned it now, and he could do with it whatever he wanted. While the submarine had once been the property of Germany, the days were sadly numbered for the Third Reich now—probably just a matter of weeks until it was all over. Thus, they would have no further need of it.

The commander, however, did have plans for its continued use. In the coming months, he would be planning meetings with a great many potential buyers. Sadly, most of them were drug kingpins and other syndicate leaders from several South American countries; but then, one had to go where the buyers were.

After the bidding for a particular treasure was completed, the highest bidder would sign a secrecy contract. Only then would the delivery of the item be arranged.

As their resources grew, they could look forward to the training of new crewmen, the future operators of the submarine. At that point, the former Kreigsmarine sailors could truly begin to think about their retirement. As for the commander, he hoped to do some traveling; but from then on it would be over the ocean, and never again beneath it. The future looked very bright indeed.

The arrival party lasted until well into the early morning. By the time dawn began to break, they'd all fallen asleep. They slept soundly for the next two days.

CHAPTER FORTY

A Horrible Arrival

I t was midnight, on April 14, 1945, when the train with its two-hundred exhausted victims finally stopped for good. If it could be called good that they had found the last concentration camp that still remained open. They had reached the camp at Bergen-Belsen, deep in Germany, a little south of Hamburg.

By then, the people inside the boxcar had become deathly silent. Most had long since given up making any sound at all. There was the occasional scream of sheer agony, that elicited little response. There was no energy left to respond with, no emotions left to feel. Their world had been reduced to pain. Only pain: physical, emotional, and intellectual. They were stunned by the extreme cruelty that fellow human beings had inflicted on them, and the casualness with which it was done.

When the rolling steel door opened at last, the soldiers who had opened it grabbed their noses and gagged at the intolerable stench that came off of the crowd.

The first to tumble out of the boxcar and into the night were Kees, Frans, Johanna, and Cornelius. They just collapsed to the ground. Their legs no longer supported them—it was the crowd in the car that had held them up. They crawled out of the way so that others might follow them out of the miserable boxcar.

Two hundred more followed from the boxcar's 10-foot by thirty-foot space. Two hundred people had been cruelly confined to the space of two bedrooms for the four days of the trip. Among them were twenty-nine who were now dead. Along the way, they had lost the will to live, and died on their feet.

The German guards shouted at the poor, stumbling, staggering victims, "Move! Clear this area! Move to the nearest barracks!" They used the butts of their guns to urge them along.

Cornelius crawled painfully on his knees across jagged gravel towards the lights of the camp. He tried to stand up, but his legs would not cooperate. All he wanted to do was lie down somewhere. In the shadows near the barracks, Cornelius saw a mountain that looked very odd, like a giant pile of sticks, but not. He wondered what kind of a mountain would be in the middle of the camp? He thought maybe he was having a bad dream.

When Cornelius had reached the barracks, he pulled himself inside and crawled over to a small window. He'd had enough of small, dark wooden rooms. He grabbed the window sill and held on to it for dear life as others crowded into the building.

Through the little barred window, he could see a huge bonfire ablaze in the middle of a field. Soldiers hurried back and forth, in and out of the light cast by the fire. They carried boxes and bags of papers and threw them into the roaring blaze. The flames flared up to high heaven each time they tossed on a new box or a bag. He wondered why they were doing that.

People continued to bump up against Cornelius as he gazed through the window, pushing past him to find someplace to live, or someplace to hide from death a little while longer. Suddenly, he felt something in his head, the lights went out, and he sank to the ground. Uncounted hours later, Cornelius woke up again. Someone had laid him on a crude wooden bunk. He had awakened to the sound of loud bangs, like cracks of thunder.

The bangs came from every direction, so Cornelius climbed out of the bunk and peered through the window. At first, everything looked the same. Then he saw them . . . tanks! There were tanks plowing through the barbed wire fences!

The German soldiers, in their gray uniforms, began to run in every direction. Behind the tanks, soldiers in green uniforms came flooding through the gaps in the fences. They wore the flatter helmets with the wide brims, so Cornelius thought they were probably British soldiers.

Sometimes the soldiers in green fired at the Nazis, but more often they just shouted for the Germans to surrender. And surrender they did. They had no interest in dying during their final minutes of the war.

"Drop your guns!" They men in green shouted, "Hands over your heads!" Now that he'd heard their voices, Cornelius knew that these were indeed British troops. The German soldiers complied with their orders meekly.

The people in the barracks began weeping and shouting for joy. "We are liberated! We are free," they cheered. "Thanks be to God, the British came to rescue us!"

Soon the shooting stopped, and the camp grew quiet. Then there was a loud crash at the door as British soldiers knocked it open with a sledge hammer. The same sound could be heard up and down the camp as other prisoners were set free.

A few British soldiers entered, then just stopped and stared in stunned silence at the sorry state of the people before them.

One of the men recovered his composure, and asked, "Does anyone in here speak English?" A few hands were raised. "Excellent. Then would you be so good as to pass along the word for us?"

Those who had raised their hands translated what was said into Dutch. "They say that we should stay inside for just a little while, until all of the Nazis have been arrested. Then they will return for us and give us food and drink. Praise God."

The people inside the barracks hugged each other tightly, as they laughed and shouted, "We are free! Free!" Some of them paused for a breath, and said in wonder, "And we're getting food. Food!" They began cheering again, "This is the greatest day of our lives!"

On April 15, 1945, the British troops found the hundreds of barracks of the Bergen-Belsen Concentration Camp. They were filled with 60,000 Jews, many from the Netherlands. All were severely malnourished, badly ill, and highly contaminated with typhus and other diseases. But those were the lucky ones.

Mountains of dead bodies were lying everywhere, and they vastly outnumbered the living. Hundreds of thousands of laughing, living, happy families had been converted to nothing more than great piles of "sticks".

As the Allies advanced into Germany, the Nazis lost all control over the horrible situation in the camps. They had cranked up the volume of executions to high gear, and no longer bothered to burn or bury the dead. They had been determined to execute their Final Solution at all costs

IT WAS HERE, at Bergen-Belsen that Anne Frank and her sister Margot had died of typhus only a few weeks before.

Bergen Belsen, shortly ater the liberation. The German soldiers are gone, but the bodies of their victims remain everywhere.

THE NAZI SOLDIERS and their officers were soon captured and disarmed, then locked up in their own living quarters. There they would be held until proper prisoner of war camps could be created to hold them for trial.

Meanwhile, the British army set up field kitchens under tents, with tables and chairs. It was time that these poor people were properly fed. But it could not be done too quickly. Many were in such an advanced state of starvation that the food would have to be parceled out slowly and carefully, until their bodies became accustomed to food again.

They brought crackers and clean water to the barracks to get the people started on the path to normal food. It was a huge undertaking—there were 60,000 starving people in the camp. Many were sick with contagious diseases, and everyone was infested with lice and fleas.

Most of the prisoners who remained were being held by the Nazis in the almost ridiculous hope of trading them for German prisoners of war. This was before the German armies collapsed in the face of the Allied advances. But there would be no negotiated exchanges now, not after what the Allies had seen. The only possible outcome was Germany's complete and unconditional surrender.

AT MIDDAY ON APRIL 15, men of the 11th Armored Division of the British Army began to register the camp prisoners. Lines were formed at tables in front of every barracks building, with British officers behind them. Kees, Johanna, and Cornelius stood before a British officer with a tablet and a pencil in hand.

"Your name, please," the officer said, preparing to write.

Kees answered promptly, "Kees van Rijn."

The officer looked up in surprise and said, "Are you the Kees van Rijn from The Hague?"

Thoroughly baffled, Kees answered, "Yes, sir. And this is my wife Johanna, and my son Cornelius. But how on earth do you know my name?"

The officer stood up from his chair and walked around the table, extending a hand. He shook hands warmly with Kees, then patted his shoulder. "Remember your radio reports to London?" the officer asked. "I wondered why you stopped broadcasting. It must have been six weeks since we talked last. I was your liaison officer at the other end."

"What a wonderful coincidence," Kees said, smiling, "but why are you over here in Germany now?"

"How long ago were you picked up by the Nazis?"

Kees told him the story of his arrest, the endless torturing, and about how Wuerff lured Johanna and his son to the jail just before shipping them all here.

"Captain Wuerff, you say? Yes, I believe he's here too," the officer said. "I've seen that name on the list of captured officers.

"I'll make a note of that, so we can add it to his war crimes file. As for the van Rijns, you, your wife, and your son need to go back to Holland right away. Are you fit to leave today?"

"Fit to leave here?" Kees said wryly, "How soon can we go?"

"I'll arrange for a truck immediately. There are plenty of supply convoys running back and forth, so it won't be hard. You're needed badly back in The Hague."

The officer waved a soldier over. A sergeant stepped up and snapped a quick salute. "Sir!"

"Sergeant, these good people need a thorough washing-up, some clean clothes, and enough food to sustain them back to Holland." He ordered, "Take very good care of them. They are important leaders of the Dutch Resistance. They will be leaving, as soon as you can arrange for a truck for them."

"It would be my pleasure, sir!"

It took the British army less than two hours to get Kees and his family cleaned, clothed, fed, and into a truck bound for home. They would leave the gruesome scene of Bergen-Belsen behind them at midnight.

Before they left, Kees returned to the liaison officer with a request. "My second in command, Frans de Ruyter, was also arrested and with us on the train. I could really use him back in Holland, but we've lost track of him. Can we try to find him?"

"We'll give you all the help you need," the officer said confidently. "If he's here, we'll find him." He wrote the name down, then called over a sergeant and gave him orders to find the man as quickly as possible.

Kees walked over to the nearest barracks, intending to start looking for Frans. Then he saw the quarantine notice tacked to the door. Kees did not dare to go inside. Many people were very sick and some were dying.

In two days, the chaos rampant in Bergen-Belsen would be brought under control, and the recovery work well organized. Specialist doctors were brought in to tend to the sick. The typhus epidemic was so severe that, even with proper medical care, many people continued to die. Two months after the liberation, the epidemic finally ended, but it had taken 30,000 people with it.

Weeks of work were required to remove thousands of bodies from the camp. The dead lay everywhere, some stacked in mountains. At first, the SS guards were used to collect and bury the bodies, but eventually they realized that heavy machinery would be required to avoid further outbreaks of disease. Bulldozers were brought in to finish the tragic and grisly work.

After his visit to the quarantined barracks, Kees returned to the liaison officer and asked again for help. "With the task ahead of us, I need Frans," Kees explained. "When all of Holland has been liberated, we'll need to find and round up the NSB-ers who betrayed so many of our citizens.

"Please, you must help us find Frans," Kees finished, "so we can take him with us to Holland."

"I do have men working on it," the officer said, "but we really should not waste any time getting you out of here."

Kees pointed at the barracks they had spent the night in, and said, "He should be over there, it's where we stayed last night. But now there are so many sick in there, that I don't dare go in."

There were sixty thousand people still alive in Bergen Belsen. The Nazis had stopped trying to take care of them at all. The British were appalled at the chaos. The prisoners needed everything, including shoes. Mountains of them had been taken from the dead.

The officer called for a medic, and sent him to the barracks. He protected himself, then went in to check on the suffering ex-prisoners. In an hour, he was back with the sad news. "I'm very sorry, sir. We found your colleague, Frans, in the barracks. The others near him tell us that he passed away only hours ago."

Kees could not help tearing up. He thought, *I'd better not tell Johanna about this, she'll be devastated.*

The truck was ready. With a heavy heart, Kees helped his family climb into the waiting truck, and they left the scene of such incredible evil behind them for good.

CHAPTER FORTY-ONE

The Nazi Round-up

T he day after the liberation of Bergen-Belsen, two platoons of British Military Police arrived at the camp. It was their task to round up and register the Nazi camp leadership, the soldiers, and the civilian employees of the camp. They would then be transferred to a special prisoner of war camp to await trial.

Many of these war criminals had no intention of facing trial for their crimes. They disappeared into the warehouses of clothing stolen from the victims of the camp. Inside, they quickly shed their uniforms and changed into civilian clothes. Emerging as "prisoners," they attempted to blend into the crowd.

In the chaos of those first moments of liberation, it was a good idea. But in time, most were exposed, discovered by their angry victims. Sometimes, it was their stolen clothing that gave them away. It wasn't worn out enough, it simply looked too new. For others, it was their hygiene, they were too well-scrubbed and clean-shaven to have been inmates. For others, it was their lack of Dutch or Yiddish language skills. Many were caught and angrily beaten by the people that they'd so horrifically abused. Then, the British soldiers took them into custody.

When the British army had first liberated the camp, they had set up a perimeter that would allow no one to escape. Some of the Nazis had tried to flee, but British infantry waiting behind the tanks had shot them.

Over the course of the brief battle for the camp, the British troops had systematically driven most of the guards and other camp personnel into the middle of a great circle. Incidentally, it was the same spot where the smoldering remnants of the camp records had burned the night before. The Nazis had surrendered quickly at that point.

The transport train, which had brought Kees and his family to this infernal place, still sat on the tracks, as if it was waiting to gather its next load of victims.

Captain Wuerff and his men had used the luxury carriage to overnight at the camp. It had been a rude awakening to them as well, when they heard the cannon fire. They had laid low and watched as the British tanks rolled in and their infantry fanned out across the camp.

Wuerff's men loaded their rifles and watched silently as the camp guards and workers were surrounded and captured. Most of the men hoped that they could slip out that night. Captain Wuerff thought it more likely that they would be shooting their way out of Bergen-Belsen.

The British commander hadn't forgotten the train, and he ordered the carriage surrounded. A patrol went forward to the locomotive, where they found the engineers cowering in fright. The two men explained about their passengers and their sleeping arrangements.

Tanks rolled up on either side, to cover the carriage. Then, the engineers were ordered to move the train outside the camp.

The commander thought it might be better to conduct any further fighting well away from the civilian prisoners. It took some time for the locomotive to build up enough steam to move, so the tanks waited patiently alongside the tracks. Killing Nazis now, or killing them later, it made no difference to them. They were good at their work.

"Call them out, sergeant," the commander ordered.

"Yes, sir!" With the help of a loudspeaker, the sergeant ordered the Germans to lay down their weapons and come out with their hands behind their heads.

Instead, several shots rang out from the carriage. No one was hit, and the siege was on.

The sergeant tried again, "Throw all of your weapons out of the windows or we will open fire."

Nothing happened.

The British commander calmly walked over to one of the tanks and called up to the tank commander. "Sergeant? Would you be so good as to put one round through the lower part of the carriage?"

"It would be my pleasure, sir." A loud bang sounded and a very large hole appeared at the bottom of the passenger car.

This time, the commander himself spoke through the loud speaker. "The next shot comes in through the windows. Throw your weapons out now, and come out with your hands in the air."

Wuerff was beside himself. "After five years of dedicated service to the Reich, this is how it all ends? No. We will fight to the finish."

His soldiers disagreed, and began to throw their guns out of the windows of the train. After all, they had been promised that they were going home. Wuerff began screaming at them. "Do

not give up your weapons, you cowards! We are to defend ourselves, and the Reich, to the end!"

One of his men walked to the end of the carriage and pulled
the door open to leave. "Heil, Hitler," Wuerff said, and shot the
man with his pistol.

The soldier tumbled out of the carriage and down to the
ground. A pair of British troopers ran forward and dragged the
wounded man to safety.

A final order sounded through the loudspeaker, "Surrender
now or we open fire." The commander signaled the tanks with
a wave. "Move forward!"

Two of the tanks rolled forward a few dozen yards, adjusting
their guns as they moved. The sound of their tracks convinced
more Nazi soldiers to throw out their guns, and several made a
rush for the door.

Wuerff raised his pistol to fire at the retreating troopers, and
one of the sergeants jumped at his captain. He landed a solid
punch on Wuerff's jaw, then twisted the pistol out of his grasp
and tossed it aside. The Captain tried to shove past him to go
for his handgun. As he did, the big sergeant simply wrapped an
elbow around his neck and pulled tightly, squeezing off his air.

Captain Wuerff struggled for a few moments, but it was to
no avail—the sergeant was simply too big. He passed out under
the strain, and a minute later all of his men were off of the train.
The sergeant dragged the Captain to the door and dumped him
unceremoniously through. He tumbled to the ground.

The German holdouts were handcuffed and led to a waiting truck, which hauled them away to a POW compound. The
Captain was carried to a makeshift clinic in the camp, where he
was tied securely to the bed.

Captain Wuerff was later brought before a British military tribunal in Luneburg, Germany. The court found him guilty of war crimes and sentenced him to twenty-five years in jail. He did not live long enough to fulfill his entire sentence.

No one ever found out what happened to the suitcase of loot that he had stolen from the people on the train.

CHAPTER FORTY-TWO

Back to the Netherlands

The British army truck was stocked with food and drink, and Kees, Johanna, and Cornelius were comfortable for the first time in a long time. The driver had driven the route several times, so the trip should have gone smoothly. But this time, he was at a loss how to get back into the Netherlands.

Most of Holland was still occupied by the German army. The eastern border with Germany was lined with bunkers and cannons. If a British army vehicle came as close as ten miles to the front lines they could be shot at.

The Canadian army held control over the northwestern part of Germany, so they kept to that area. From Bergen-Belsen, the driver headed due south. He had tried several times to go west, back to the Netherlands, but each time they were turned back. "You don't want to go that way, son," a grizzled Canadian sergeant had told them. "Holland is still thick with Nazis."

Several times, the British truck was stopped and thoroughly searched, while Kees and his little family patiently waited. The Allied advance had penetrated far into Germany, and they were on the lookout for saboteurs and escaping Nazis. The driver had

231

to show his orders frequently at checkpoints before they were allowed to continue on.

As they drove across the countryside, Cornelius slept on their laps while Kees and Johanna looked out the windows. All along the route, the cities and towns had suffered battle damage. Some of the larger cities lay in complete ruin, while smaller towns and villages looked almost untouched.

White sheets and flags could sometimes be seen hanging in the windows of the undamaged towns. Clearly, many of the German civilians were ready to be finished with the war. But not all of them. Shattered towns testified of fanatical holdouts who had to be rooted out with fierce firefights.

The larger cities, especially the industrial cities of the Rhur valley, had been nearly flattened by heavy bombers of the Allied air forces. Between the British at night, and Americans by day, thousands of Allied planes crossed the skies over Germany, laying waste to their war production plants, as well as the cities that surrounded them.

The cities along the route to Holland, like Bremen, Dortmund, Dusseldorf, and Essen, seemed to have no inhabitants left at all. Scattered survivors could be seen here and there, picking through the rubble. Kees was in awe of the devastation that had been unleashed. What was Hitler thinking? He'd brought ruin to much of Europe, but now most especially to Germany.

Scores of bombers were shot down by German anti-aircraft artillery, but not enough to stop the destruction. The pilots and crews often parachuted to safety. If they bailed out over German territory, they were usually captured and taken to prisoner-of-war camps. But many of the crews had been able to hide during the day and walk at night, making their way west to the Netherlands. There, the Resistance had given the men refuge at Dutch farms, until they could be smuggled back to England.

The battle zones were awash in army vehicles. Jeeps, trucks, cannons, and tanks, mostly Canadian, could be seen everywhere they looked. Convoys rolled towards the front, and green vehicles dotted every field and town. The Allies were everywhere it seemed—or at least all over this part of Germany.

Where the Allies were not was in the Netherlands. Part of the country in the south had been liberated, but most of it still remained tightly under Nazi control. Kees was eager to enter the Netherlands, but the German forces were well positioned and heavily armed.

April was in its final days, and Germany was beginning to crumble. In Kees' opinion, the time was ripe for an attack. But first, they had to find a weak point. Their truck had to go all the way south to Belgium.

When they reached the outskirts of Antwerp, the driver stopped at a sentry post to find out how they could get into Holland. The sentry said, "Not much chance of that, buddy.

"The Schelde River is the battle line, there's no way you can cross that river. The line of battle is from twenty miles north all the way to the border with Germany.

"The Nazis created a water barrier by busting the dykes of the Rhine. And they have a row of bunkers with big guns that we can't penetrate. Not unless we bomb them."

"What do you want to do, sir?" the driver asked Kees.

"I have no idea. We'll have to find another way in."

"We're waiting for the Navy to come up the Schelde River and take care of those guns," the sentry said. "Soon, we'll take Holland from the Nazis. Until then, you'll have to wait here."

Kees looked at the driver, who only shrugged and said, "I can drop you off somewhere, sir. But I can't wait around too long. Do you know anyone here with a place where you can stay? At least, I can take you there."

Kees thought about the Resistance connections that he had in Belgium. Suddenly, he remembered, "I know of a church in Zavelte. It used to be our meeting place whenever we had to take people through France to Switzerland. Can you drive us? I can find a place to stay there."

"I most certainly can, sir," their driver said.

By the time they reached the church in Zavelte, it was 5:30 a.m. on the 17th of April. The town was still sound asleep, not one person was out and about yet. The driver dropped them off at the church as the sky began to lighten in the east.

"Good luck to you, my friends. Perhaps we'll see each other again in Holland someday soon." He waved a goodbye, and the truck roared away.

They sat on the steps outside the church and waited. It wasn't until 7:00 a.m. that they saw the first person out on the street. Kees called the gentleman over and asked if he knew where the pastor of the church could be found. The man looked Kees right in the eyes, and said, "Kees van Rijn?! I'm the pastor, Kees. Don't you remember?"

Kees' face lit up in recognition, "Oh, yes! Yes, I do! Now I remember, pastor. We've been through such an ordeal these past six days that my memory is a bit fuzzy."

"Why don't you come inside, and you can tell me all about it. Perhaps you might like some breakfast too?"

"And coffee?" Kees asked, "We sure need it! Breakfast would be wonderful—the best thing we've had in weeks."

This church in Zavelte was a center of the Belgian Resistance and helped transport Jews to Switzerland and Spain.

The pastor's wife set to work in the kitchen, and produced breakfast in minutes. After the week they'd had, it smelled like the finest gourmet cooking in the world. While the van Rijn family enjoyed their feast, Kees told them everything about the past few weeks. He started with his arrest and ended with the miracle of meeting his liaison officer from England.

"God was with you all the time, Kees," the pastor said. "Now you will be able to glorify Him for the rest of your life."

Cornelius listened patiently while Kees told the pastor about the horrible events, then he felt that it was his turn to talk. "But

235

Dad," he began, "you haven't told him everything. Tell him about how Mom and me cleaned you up after the torture. And how they tricked mom and me, to take us on the train too. . . .

"And tell him about how we all had to go to the bathroom in our pants . . . and about all of those poor people who died on the train. Go on, tell him."

"I think you just told it pretty well, Cornelius," Kees said, "You must never forget those things, my son. You'll be able to tell these stories for many years. You are a key witness to it all."

"Kees, Johanna," the pastor suddenly asked, "when was the last time you slept? You probably haven't seen a nice, soft bed in a very long time."

Johanna was quick to answer, "You're right, I can't remember the last time we really slept. We never could, not even in the barracks at the camp."

"Well, we have the perfect beds for you," the pastor offered. "You'll need the energy before you can walk back to The Hague."

"That sounds marvelous," Johanna replied. "We'll probably sleep for days once we hit the sheets."

The pastor's wife ushered them up the stairs which led to the master bedroom. "Please, you must use our room. It's very quiet, and I just changed the sheets. Go on, make yourselves at home, and sleep as long as you will."

When she came back downstairs the pastor's wife said to her husband, "You'd better contact some Resistance men. We need to find a way for this family to get back into Holland."

CHAPTER FORTY-THREE

Back to the War in Holland

ornelius was the first one to wake up, three days later. He looked around the strange room, wondering where he was. Then he saw his parents sound asleep in the big bed. Was he dreaming?

It was all so different and unknown to him. Cornelius decided to wake up his Dad and ask if everything was real, or if they were in heaven.

He shook his father's arm, and said "Daddy, wake up! We are somewhere else, not in the confrontation camp any longer. Where are we, Dad? Wake up!"

Kees woke slowly, and looked around the room. Then he smiled, and said: "We're at a church in Belgium, remember?"

Cornelius nodded. "Okay. Yes, now I remember. But how did we get into these beds? When did we come here?"

"What did you just call it, son? I heard you say 'confrontation camp?' The word is 'concentration camp'!" Kees began to laugh, "Confrontation camp! Ha! That's funny. But even so, you know you're right? It was a confrontation camp for us!" He laughed and ruffled his son's hair.

Johanna woke up from all of the confrontation and laughter, and sat up. She rubbed her eyes and asked, "Where are we? What time is it?" She shook her head, "I wonder what day it is. I'm so confused. I never changed clothes. Did we sleep all dressed?"

Kees climbed out of the bed. "I'll look around and see what I can find out."

As he did, it all came back to him. They were at the pastor's house in Zavelte. The pastor had given them his own bedroom. They must have slept for days. He walked down the stairs, and found the pastor and his wife sitting at the large kitchen table. They said simultaneously. "Well, look who's up!" The pastor asked, "Do you know how long you've all slept?"

Kees shook his head, "I have no idea, please tell me."

"You arrived here early in the morning on April 16th. Today, it is the 19th, and it's five o'clock in the morning. Kees, you and your family have slept for three days and three nights. You might call that hibernation!"

All Kees could say was, "Wow." He nodded, "We needed it."

Johanna and Cornelius came downstairs and followed Kees into the kitchen. Their clothes were all wrinkled, and Johanna was embarrassed. "Good morning, I'm sorry about my looks. We haven't a change of clothes with us. I don't even have a brush to run through my hair."

The pastor's wife stood up from the kitchen table, and said, "Come, I'll help you. We'll get you a hot shower, and I'll find you a nice dress to wear." She put an arm around Johanna. "You know, if I had slept for three days and nights, I would look much worse."

"Are you joking? Did we really sleep so long? We must have been exhausted, but didn't really know it till we hit the pillows."

In a sleepy voice, Cornelius said, "I am so hungry, I could eat a whole cow."

Later that morning, two men arrived from the Belgian Resistance. They came to see the pastor, and to advise Kees on what his options were to get into Holland.

Kees knew these men, having worked with them several times on previous escapes. They'd helped many Dutch Jews escape to Switzerland. The men were highly skilled in transportation, knowing every Nazi roadblock, and every back road that would bypass them. They had moved all about Belgium, right under the eyes of the Gestapo. Now that the war was over in Belgium, they spent their time catching former collaborators.

"Let's talk about your upcoming return to Holland," one of the men began. They had brought a map which they spread out across the table. Pointing out where the German lines were, they covered the options they had to get Kees back into Holland undetected. "Allied ships are up in the North Sea," he pointed, "and down here, in the English Channel at the Dover Strait. The Allies are ready to sail up the Schelde River. The only thing holding them up are big enemy bunkers on the shores of Zeeland at the mouth of the river.

"Before they can sail to Antwerp, the cannons in those bunkers have to be destroyed. Thousands of paratroopers landed behind the lines to hit the cannons from behind. The southwestern part of Zeeland has been cleared of Nazis. Within a day or two, the liberation of Holland will begin."

"This is good news," Kees said. "But how do we get in while all of that is going on?"

"We can take you into liberated Zeeland by rowboat, crossing the Schelde behind the first group of Navy ships. We'll have

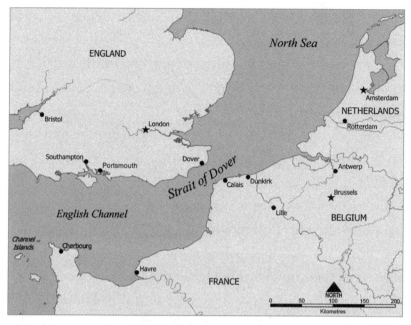

Hundreds of Allied warships were close at hand in The North Sea and the English Channel, ready to aid in the liberation of Holland.

to notify Navy command that we'll be bringing you across. We don't want any patrol boats to mistake you for Nazis and blow you out of the water."

"I would appreciate that, "Kees grinned.

"We'll make the crossing at night. Nazi snipers are still out there, and they may not care for us crossing into their territory. So, we suggest that you make preparations to go tonight, provided we get the okay from the Navy. If not, you'll have to wait one more day."

"We'll be ready," Kees said, already itching to go.

"Take it easy the rest of this day. Get plenty of food and rest," the Resistance man encouraged Kees. "Remember, you'll be back in the war for some days to come. The Nazis are still in charge of most of the Netherlands."

"Thank God, not for long," Kees replied. The men smiled, shook hands, and left.

When the door closed behind them, Kees breathed a big sigh, and said "God will be with us. He'll keep us safe from the cruel hands of the Nazis."

"He has done so for five years," Johanna agreed, "even when we went through the hell of the concentration camp. We will trust in the Lord, always. Amen."

They did not get a go-ahead from the Navy that day, so they enjoyed another good night of sleep, and a couple of delicious, filling meals courtesy of the pastor and his wife. The next day, the two Belgians came to get them. "We have a car to drive you to the town of Breskens. That should be the easy part, it will take us about three hours.

"At midnight, we're scheduled to meet a British launch which will bring you all to Vlissingen (Flushing). Once there, you'll be on your own.

"Be very careful crossing the lines. The Allied soldiers will try to stop you for your own safety. Once you get through the lines, you can expect roadblocks again, just as before. Don't underestimate the Nazis. Even with the war winding down, there are still lots of fanatics among them."

Even though the old Citroen Deux Chevaux couldn't go any faster than forty kilometers per hour, they arrived early, at 11:15 p.m. There was very little traffic on the roads. Several military columns passed by, bringing thousands of troops forward to prepare for the liberation of Zeeland.

Once they arrived, Kees thanked the two Belgians who had driven them so far. "I hope to see you again, when this terrible ordeal is nothing but history. Thank you for all you have done."

The pastor's wife had made them stacks of sandwiches, which she packed in a makeshift backpack, along with two large glass bottles of cold tea. A dozen army-issue bars of chocolate completed their food supply, for who knew how many days to come.

Two sailors met them at the very busy harbor in the town of Breskens. One of them gave a short lecture on the dangers involved in riding in the small boat that would take them back to occupied Holland. "There are still enemy snipers out there, even in liberated Zeeland, who would not hesitate to take a shot at you," the sailor finished, "so we have flak jackets and helmets for you to wear on the crossing."

The voyage on the small boat lasted nearly three hours. The noise of the engine was enough to keep anyone from talking, so they rode in silence. Cornelius even napped for a little while.

As they slowed down to approach the shore, the noise of the engine lowered dramatically. "Where exactly are you dropping us off?" Kees asked.

"We'll put you ashore at Zoutelande, and you can walk from there to Middelburg. We understand there is a Resistance unit there who can help you get to The Hague."

The town of Zoutelande was well known to Kees. At the beginning of the war, they'd shipped many Jews from there to England via fishing boat.

The boat made a number of successful crossings, delivering refugees to the white cliffs of Dover. Upon one return, they were boarded by sailors from a Nazi patrol boat. In their search of the boat, they had found suspicious evidence that passengers had been transported on the fishing craft. The boat was confiscated and the fisherman was sent to the labor camps. He never returned to Zoutelande.

The other fishermen were understandably intimidated, just as the Nazis intended. No one else proved willing to assist the Resistance after that, and further refugee transports directly to England were suspended.

Kees knew where the man had lived so, after wading ashore, the little family walked over to the house where the fisherman used to live.

It was 4:30 in the morning, and the sky had not even begun to lighten yet. Kees decided not to wake anyone up until it was a decent time. They found a park bench and settled down to wait for sunrise. Even in the dark, it was a beautiful morning to them, the three sojourners breathed in the fresh air of freedom for the first time in many years.

There were no soldiers in the streets, and no German army vehicles passed by. At the moment, all was peaceful. "Freedom here in Zeeland," Kees said with a big smile. "We'd better enjoy it while we can. Soon we'll be back in our war-torn land again." He frowned, "But mark my words, not for long!"

Two hours later, a few people began to appear on the streets. One or two glanced at the disheveled family on the park bench, and shook their heads in pity at the poor "refugee" family.

Finally, a young man approached them. "Are you lost here?" He asked compassionately, "How can I help you?"

"Well, thank you for your concern," Kees answered. "We're waiting for an appropriate hour to visit the house where Piet Murre used to live."

"'Used to live,' you say? That's quite a coincidence, because Piet returned home only yesterday, and the whole town celebrated his arrival."

"How do you know him?" Kees asked.

"Piet Murre is my neighbor," the man said. "Would you like me to take you to them? I'm sure they're up by now."

The young man offered to carry their backpack, and waved the van Rijn family to follow him. Then he turned back and said, "I warn you, please try not to look too alarmed when you see him. You may not even recognize him. Piet is worn down to nothing but skin and bone."

CHAPTER FORTY-FOUR

A Surprising Reunion

I t was a walk of only two blocks on that glorious morning of temporary freedom. The front door was open, as it used to be before the war. Kees pushed the brass doorbell and they heard the chimes inside. A woman with a friendly face came to the door, and said, "Oh my, you look like you've all had a very hard time. How can we help you poor people?"

A voice behind her shouted exultantly, "Kees van Rijn! From The Hague! What on earth brings you here, so far from home?" Piet Murre asked, "And why do you look like you came straight out of a concentration camp?"

"Because we did come straight out of a concentration camp!" Kees smiled sadly, "and the past ten days have been both heaven and hell."

"Come on inside," Piet said, embracing Kees warmly. "What are we doing, standing here at the door?" He put an arm around Johanna and a hand on Cornelius' shoulder. "Come in, we'll get you some breakfast and coffee; then you can tell us all about your ten days of heaven and hell."

They had plenty to talk about at breakfast.

"Piet, you first," Kees said, as they sat down at the big table in the kitchen. "How did you survive two-and-a-half years of slave labor? And how did you manage to get back home?"

"I made myself indispensable. I became responsible for providing food to the slave labor, in place of the Nazis. They didn't want to do the job, so they did it poorly. They didn't care." Piet paused, frowning at the table as he remembered the terrible conditions. Then he looked up at Kees. "I cared, so I volunteered. We were able to feed the people a bit better, and the Nazis didn't have to do the work. So I made the slaves happier, and pleased the Nazis at the same time."

Piet smiled broadly then. "Oh, we didn't eat well—just look at me! But at least we ate, and we managed to keep some people alive a little longer. Long enough for some of them to see the end of the war anyway."

"That is truly wonderful," Kees said, "You were doing God's work for those people. But how did you get home?"

"One day the Nazis allowed me to use a truck to gather supplies for them. By then, everyone knew the Allies were getting close. So instead of picking up supplies, I drove the truck to the front lines. Piet grinned triumphantly. "I donated it to the first Allied troops that I found, on the condition that they'd send me home to Zoutelande. End of story. Now, tell us yours."

KEES BEGAN HIS STORY, by starting with Captain Wuerff. "This Nazi was so motivated to nail us, that he put two trucks and sixteen soldiers on my trail for a month. It only got worse from there. Like a good Nazi, he hated the Jews, and the Resistance, and his hatred drove him.

"They were pretty good. For a while, I didn't even know I was being followed. Once I caught on, I was able to lead them on for weeks, but finally they caught up with me.

"They were determined to fill one final train to the concentration camps. We were determind to prevent it. My friend, Frans, and I were always a few steps ahead of them."

"That's good," Piet said admiringly.

"A group of seventy-two Jews were almost caught hiding at a big chicken farm," Kees continued. "We moved them around for days, from place to place. But a dirty NSB-er led the Nazis to our group.

"They almost caught us. But the farmer stampeded his herd, and we slipped away while the Nazis were distracted. We jumped into a stinking dung cellar, and waited all night until the trucks were gone."

"Oh, I'll bet that was a fun night," Piet said wryly. Johanna simply listened in open-mouthed astonishment.

"I've had better nights," Kees replied. "What we didn't know was that the Nazis had left four soldiers behind to wait. We came out of the cellar, covered in the disgusting stuff, and looked for a hose to wash it all off. Suddenly, we were surrounded by those four Germans! . . . At least they let us hose off first, before they took us away."

"Oh, my poor dear," Johanna said as she put a hand on his forearm, "I had no idea."

"It didn't seem worth mentioning," Kees replied, as he put his hand over hers. "Not after everything else that happened."

"What else happened?" Piet prompted.

"They dropped us off at the Oranje Hotel in Scheveningen." Piet only shook his head at the news. He knew what it meant.

"For five days, Frans and I were beaten and tortured. Fists, boots, whips, you name it. It was so bad that I couldn't stand up anymore from the pain. I never gave in, and the Nazis probably would have killed me.

"But Frans made a deal with them. They were after a list of our hiding places—to fill that last train of theirs. So Frans gave them what they asked for."

Piet frowned at that. "He gave up the Jews?"

"No. Frans would never do that. He gave the Nazis a list of addresses where Jews had been hidden; but they were all places that he knew were empty." Kees smiles sadly, shaking his head in admiration. "It was quite clever. I wish I had thought of it sooner, but I was more than a little muddled by then.

"I guess he thought they wouldn't hold it against us if they turned up empty-handed. We were in jail, how would we have known? I still think they would have killed us."

"They tried to," Johanna added.

"You're right, of course," Kees said. "They did, just not the way I expected."

"What do you mean?" Piet asked, "What did they do?"

"Apparently, they gave up on us after visiting the addresses on Frans' list. So they tried a new angle. On the sixth day, they sent soldiers to Johanna and told her her that she could visit the jail to see me—to bring clean clothes and wash me up. She couldn't leave Cornelius at home, so she brought him, too."

Kees reached over for Cornelius, and lifted him out of his chair and held him on his lap. "I felt so bad that my little boy should see his father in such terrible condition." Kees kissed his son on the top of his head. "Once Johanna and Cornelius had fixed me up, she called the guard and asked for a truck to take us home. They brought us a truck, all right; but it didn't take us home. They dropped us at the train station and shoved us into an overloaded boxcar. The last one, I think."

Piet foully questioned the guards' parentage for a moment, then apologized to Cornelius for his coarse language. The boy only grinned appreciatively.

"It was four days of hell on earth in that car," Kees went on. "We arrived at Bergen-Belsen, exhausted, filthy, and starving. It was the last concentration camp that was still open. Even in the dark, we could see mountains of bodies everywhere. We crawled away from the train—because our legs would no longer carry us—into a barracks that was already full of people.

"The next morning, a true miracle occurred," Kees said as he teared up. "We heard shots, then tanks and trucks of the British army rolled through the fences into the camp. Nazi soldiers were running in every direction, but soon they were captured and locked away."

"That is a miracle, indeed," Piet replied soberly. "How you have been blessed."

"I think we were doubly blessed," Kees said. "The train that brought us still sat on the tracks. The captain who had hunted us down, Wuerff, was still in the passenger car with his men. There was a little more fighting, then we saw them arrested as well."

"So your Captain Wuerff got what he deserved at last," Piet said with some satisfaction.

"I think so," Kees said, smiling now. "I hope so. The British gave us food and drink, and then set up tables and began to register everyone in the camp. When it was our turn, an officer asked for my name. When I gave it, he looked up in surprise and said, 'Are you the Kees van Rijn from The Hague?'"

"You're kidding," Piet said. "How did he know your name?"

"That's just what I asked him," Kees replied. "He was my radio contact in England, the army liaison officer on the other end! He arranged a truck for us, and got us back to Belgium."

"God works in mysterious ways," Piet said in awe.

"So now, with the help of the Royal Navy," Kees said, "we're here with you. And we're ready to go home."

"I think we can help."

CHAPTER FORTY-FIVE

Through the War Zone

P iet stood up and began to slowly circle around the large table as he thought out loud. "We have to get you back on the road, but you'll have to go across the front lines. It could be dangerous. You'll be traveling through occupied territory again, too. Are you ready for that?"

Kees nodded, "I understand, and we are ready to go. Aren't we?" he asked his wife and son. Johanna nodded seriously.

"Let's go home!" Cornelius said excitedly. "I have things I have to do!" This sparked a round of chuckling.

"Yes, I think we all do," Kees smiled. "I have a number of Resistance contacts on the way. We just need some directions and a little help to find our way through."

"Kees, how would you like a box-bicycle for your trip?" Piet asked. "We have one that you could take. It would allow you to move much faster than walking. Johanna and Cornelius can ride inside, and it has a double-bottom where you can hide some extra clothing."

"Why would we need to hide extra clothing?" Kees asked, frowning. "It's not contraband or anything."

A Dutch box-bicycle. Picture one "woman" pedaling, and another woman riding in the box with a little boy, through a hundred of miles of war-torn Holland.

"Because you'll be traveling in disguise," Piet said. "I don't think it's a good idea for you to go roaming about occupied territory as a male."

"Oh, no," Kees sighed, "here we go again."

"The Nazis have been taking away every man over sixteen to be used as forced labor," Piet explained. "You might think, with the war nearing its end, that kind of thing would be all over. But I wouldn't want you to take the chance."

"No. I agree with you completely," Kees said. "It was only last week that the Nazis were still rounding up Jews. The Allies have crossed the Rhine and are racing through Germany, and still they're at it."

"Some people just don't know when to quit," Johanna said.

Piet nodded, and said, "With the double-bottom in the box-bicycle, you can keep your male clothes hidden, just in case you need them. But during the trip, I think we'll disguise you as a woman." Piet smiled, "Sadly, not a very pretty one."

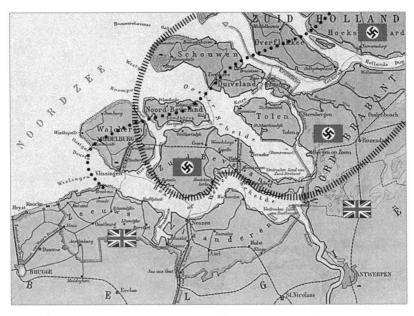

The battle lines in Zeeland, during the last month of the war. The dotted line shows the route Kees took from Belgium, through the freed zone of Zeeland, and into occupied territory on the way back to The Hague.

"Well, looks like it'll be just us girls," Kees said to Johanna.

"Do I have to go in disguise, too?" Cornelius asked.

"No," Johanna said, as she ruffled his hair. "You're perfect just the way you are." Cornelius grinned as he smoothed his hair down again.

"We'll have to get an *Ausweiss* for each one of you," Piet said. "We have someone in town who can make them, but it will take a few hours. I'll go see him now."

"Well, you've only been home a day, Piet," Kees said, "and you're right back in the thick of things again."

"As are you, my friend. You're all welcome to stay and spend the night. It will give us time to get everything ready, including your disguise. Do you need anything while I'm out? Perhaps something to color your hair?"

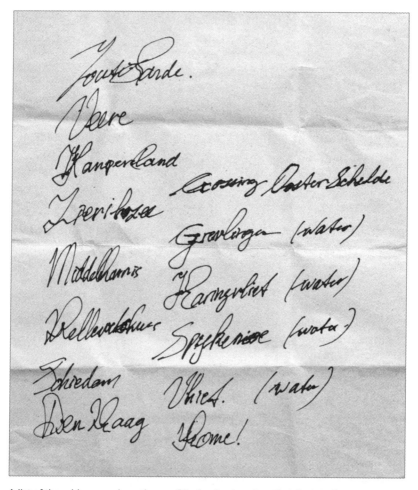

A list of the addresses where the van Rijn family stayed on their journey home.

They all laughed, which eased the tension a little. Piet left, but he was back again a few minutes later, riding the promised box-bicycle. "You know how to handle one of these, right?"

Kees was all too familiar with them, as was Cornelius, having ridden along on many a mission. "Yes, thank you. I'm pretty sure we'll be okay. Won't we, son?"

"It looks a lot like our bike at home, Dad," Cornelius said.

"It does indeed! I think we'll know just what to do."

By the time the preparations were complete, it was 5:00 p.m. "It's too late to leave today," Piet said. "When you cross the lines in Veere, the Germans will never let you through. It will be curfew by then.

"You should leave bright and early at 6 o'clock in the morning. By the time you're there, the roadblocks will be open and soldiers will be bored. They'll glance at your IDs and just wave you on through."

"I hope so," Johanna said nervously, "I wouldn't care to be arrested again. Especially now, so close to the end. I don't think we could be so lucky again."

"If anyone asks, tell them you're going home to Zierikzee," Piet said. "That will be the address on your IDs."

"Not to worry, my dear," Kees said, "I've done this sort of thing before."

"So have I!" Cornelius added, and Johanna smiled, reassured.

"Tonight, my wife will treat you to a farewell dinner, then Kees can put up his hair, and you can all get a good night's sleep!"

"Funny, Piet. Typical sailor's humor. How will we manage on this trip without your sparkling wit?" Kees smiled, then asked, "Do you have a piece of paper and a pencil? I would like to map out a route to The Hague, and make a list of the places where we might be able to stay overnight."

"Kees, my friend, all that I have is yours."

CHAPTER FORTY-SIX

Traveling on a Box-Bicycle

I t was seven long days and nights before the van Rijn family finally reached their home in The Hague. They passed through many road blocks without incident, pedaling through ten towns and crossing several wide rivers to arrive at their destination: Home Sweet Home.

Kees' many Resistance friends helped them to overcome the obstacles on their journey. They crossed the widest of rivers on fishing boats, and the narrower spans on hand-pulled ferries. Generously, they found the van Rijns a place to sleep each night, and fed them as well as they were able. Thanks to his time with the Dutch Resistance in The Hague, Kees was known in many of the towns that they visited. Sometimes his friends were surprised by his disguise as a woman; but most understood the drastic measures the resistance fighters had to take to survive.

As it turned out, the worst part of the trip was pedaling a box-bicycle loaded with passengers for over a hundred miles. Kees' legs were tired, and he slept well each night.

Their travels took place under the eyes of watchful Nazi soldiers, who were still on duty everywhere. While that had become a fact of life over the last several years, it felt odd somehow now. Knowing as they did how Germany was collapsing, it was strange to see the Nazi soldiers still going about their business, calmly maintaining order. They never questioned or searched Kees and his family—the soldiers had no interest in two ladies and a child. It was clear that the war was coming to an end. The soldiers were more relaxed and even tried to befriend the citizens.

Over the many miles, the box-bicycle served them very well. It gave them not a bit of trouble, so they traveled as long and as far as they could each day. It was midnight when the van Rijns rolled onto the driveway of the Brandwijk farm.

The farmer's family would be sound asleep, but Kees knew a special code that he could knock on the front door of the farmhouse. The code would tell the farmer that there was no cause for alarm. Kees tapped it out, and in a few minutes the farmer came to the door, not even surprised that a visitor would arrive at such a late hour.

Cor Brandwijk opened the door, and cried out in surprise, "Whoa! Are you a ghost from the past? Is this for real?" He reached out and grabbed Kees by the shoulders. "We thought you were sent to a concentration camp! How on earth did you get back here?" He shook Kees' hand enthusiastically, then hugged him tight.

In the excitement, Cor had forgotten to invite Kees and his family inside. Finally, he realized what he'd done, "Oh! I should invite you all inside! Come, come!" He herded them indoors. "I guess we have a lot to talk about."

They all went into the traditional upper-room, common to every farm, that was used for important visitors. In some places, it was called *de mooie kamer* (the beautiful room). Johanna and

Cornelius settled down on the large sofa and huddled together. They fell asleep in a matter of minutes, exhausted from the long and challenging trip.

Kees and Cor Brandwijk settled into a couple of comfortble chairs, and Kees stretched out, sighing in relief. He told the farmer their entire story, from his arrest all the way to their liberation from the concentration camp. The two men were close friends, and they talked for hours, exchanging stories about their work with the Resistance. They enjoyed a couple of drinks while they talked, and finally Kees began to grow sleepy.

"Why don't you get some sleep now, Kees? You still have a long way to go before you reach The Hague," Cor said. "You need your rest."

"That sounds like an excellent idea," Kees said, pulling up a footstool. "I think I'll just stretch out right here."

"No, no. We have a bedroom for you all. Let's move your family there so you'll sleep more comfortably." Cor gently woke up Johanna while Kees lifted Cornelius into his arms. "Normally, I'd be getting up pretty soon to milk the cows," Cor said. "But since the Nazis took them, there's nobody to milk. So I think I'll go back to sleep, too."

They woke up to the sound of pots and pans rattling in the kitchen, and the delicious smell of something warm and filling. Mrs. Brandwijk was preparing breakfast. They cleaned up a bit then joined Cor and his wife at the table.

"Where is Marie?" Cor asked his wife. "Isn't she hungry?"

"She was up long ago," Mrs. Brandwijk said. "She's already eaten and gone off to see her friends."

They were all chatting together and enjoying the fine breakfast, when Mrs. Brandwijk said, "What on earth is that noise?"

"It looks like some kind of an odd parade," Cor said, as he peered through the window of the upper room. "I wonder why they would be coming here?" Everyone else pushed back their chairs and joined Cor in looking outside. Naturally, Cornelius got there first.

A large group of people were approaching the farm, moving about wildly. In the distance, they seemed to be dancing, and skipping, and running. There was much cheering and waving of arms, and even some singing could be heard. Many of the revelers were waving flags large and small, and others were blowing noisily on paper horns.

"Let's go outside and see why they're putting on such a lively show," Cor said.

"I wonder if this is what I think it is?" Kees replied, as the two families stepped out onto the porch. As the crowd came closer, Kees said, "I think they're cheering about Hitler."

They were all shouting: "Hitler is dead and the war is over!" The Brandwijks' daughter, Marie, dashed ahead of the group and came running up to the porch. A long-time friend of Cornelius, she took him by the hand and pulled him away, singing, "He's dead! He's dead! Hitler's gone and dead!"

The visiting crowd approached, laughing and singing. One man shouted, "We are free! Hitler is dead and we are free again!" Another cried out, "The Nazis are leaving! Come out and celebrate with us!"

Marie pulled Cornelius toward the stable where bunches of orange marigolds were already in full bloom. "Come on, Cornelius! Let's pick flowers!" she cheered. "We'll hand them out to everyone, and they'll pin them on to celebrate the Queen coming back to Holland."

Cornelius and Marie plucked the flowers frantically, gathering up armfuls of them. The raced back to the crowd, and Marie cried out, "Marigolds for the Queen!"

Every one of the revelers wanted a brilliant orange flower of their own. Wildly waving hands reached out to the children, and Cornelius and Marie happily placed one into each palm. Cornelius thought that it was a lot like handing out their Johanna cookies, but much more fun.

When the group left, they were all waving their orange flowers in the air and singing. It was the first wild celebration of the liberation, and the people reveled in their patriotism.

It was also slightly premature. The war was not officially over yet, and they would find that out soon.

CHAPTER FORTY-SEVEN

Hitler Commits Suicide

All across Europe, the news spread that Hitler was dead. In every country, in every city, town, and village, the people went out onto the streets and joyously celebrated at the German Fuerher's death. No one shed a tear for Adolf. While the war was not quite over yet, even German soldiers celebrated along with the citizens.

On April 2, 1945, Hitler had proudly announced to the world that he had completed the so-called *Endlösung* (the Final Solution) or the successful annihilation of the Jewish people. Then, less than a month later, on April 30, 1945, he showed that he was unwilling to face the wrath of his enemies, who were approaching their own *Endlösung* of his war.

Hitler had married his longtime companion, Eva Braun, only the day before. With the Soviet armies less than a mile from the *Fuehrerbunker* in Berlin, Hitler locked himself and his newly wedded bride into his personal study. An hour later, his soldiers heard a gunshot from the room. They opened the study door to find their Fuehrer, and the new Mrs. Hitler, dead on a sofa. The burnt almond scent of cyanide could be smelled in the air.

Thus ended the mighty Third Reich.

Hitler had given instructions to his soldiers that their bodies were to be burned after their deaths, so they would not fall into enemy hands and be desecrated. The corpses were carried out of the bunker and up to the surface, where they were laid in a shell crater behind the Reich Chancellery. They were doused with petrol and lit on fire.

Several of Hitler's inner circle—those who were still left in Berlin—came upstairs to witness the end. They raised their arms in salute as the bodies burned, then turned and went downstairs, back into the *Fuehrerbunker*. Soon, most of them would die at their own hands as well. Others would be killed trying to escape Berlin, or face trial for war crimes.

Joseph Goebbels, the propaganda minister for the Reich, was one of Hitler's greatest admirers and closest friends. He and his wife would take their own lives the very next day, after first taking those of their six children.

Adolf and Eva's bodies burned incompletely, and more petrol was needed to finish the job. But with the collapse of the German defenses, there was little to be found. Hitler's men spent the next couple of hours siphoning gasoline from ruined trucks and other vehicles, then dousing and relighting the bodies again and again. When they had done the best they could, the shell hole was filled in and the charred remains were covered.

BEFORE HE DIED, Hitler had named Admiral Karl Doenitz, the Commander of the German Navy, as his successor. Hitler was under a delusion that Doenitz would still be able to win the war. However, Doenitz knew better. He established the new government in Flensburg, at the northern tip of Germany, near Denmark. The Flensburg government last for a week, as Doenitz tried to negotiate a partial surrender to the western Allies.

The negotiations were intended to stall for extra time, allowing German troops and refugees to flee to the west, where they could surrender to Allied units, and avoid capture by the Soviet Red Army. The tactic was only partially successful, lasting only a day or two, but it allowed nearly two million German soldiers to surrender to the Allies.

Admiral Doenitz was the leader of Hitler's vaunted "Thousand Year Reich" for just one week. Fortunately, his dream fell about 988 years short of his goal.

Admiral Doenitz surrendered quietly to the Allies on May 7, with all forces to cease active operations on May 8. He then signed again for the Soviets the next day. At the Nuremberg Trials, he was convicted of waging aggressive war, and sentenced to ten years in prison. He was released and lived quietly as a writer until he died at age 89.

MYSTERY SURROUNDED the circumstances of Hitler's death for some time. Absent an easily identified body, many believed that Hitler had faked his own death. To this day, some believe that he fled Germany instead, and lived out his life for many years in exile, possibly even hidden by the Allies. This myth was only Soviet state-sponsored disinformation, intended to sow mistrust among the nations of the West.

In reality, the remains of the Hitlers were discovered two days after their deaths by Soviet counterintelligence agents. They were eventually reburied in unmarked graves beneath the front courtyard of a new Soviet counterintelligence facility in Magdeburg, East Germany.

In 1970, the Soviets exhumed the remains, reburned them, and scattered them in a tributary to the Elbe River.

CHAPTER FORTY-EIGHT

Coming Home

Kees climbed onto his box-bicycle once more, on the morning of the premature celebration. Their final ride to The Hague would take only an hour and a half. Johanna was eager to return home, to resume normal life again. Cornelius wondered about his garden, and the flowers he had grown in the backyard. It had rained overnight and the streets were wet the whole trip home. Cornelius hoped it had fallen on his plants.

When Kees pedaled past the Ypenburg airport, he reflected on the many times he had been there before. Right under the noses of the Nazis, they had used the Germans' own vehicles and equipment to help many Jews escape captivity and death.

Suddenly, they heard the sound of airplane engines coughing to life at the airport they'd just passed. The noise grew and grew until it seemed like dozens of planes must rise from the airport. And rise they did. Large German transport planes roared off of the runway and turned to fly in every direction, many swooping low over the city.

The van Rijns were watching the closest planes fly past, when Kees noticed something fall from one of the planes. It scattered into thousands of pieces of white that fluttered gently down to the ground.

"What are they doing, dad?" Cornelius asked.

"Let's go find out," Kees said, as he pushed off the bike and began to pedal. Papers of some sort whirled down on the wind, all across the city. Everywhere the planes went, the clouds of white followed below and behind.

Kees hurried his family over to a neighborhood where the papers were still falling to the ground. He grabbed one from the air and read it aloud:

WARNING! THE WAR IS NOT OVER.

THE THIRD REICH HAS A NEW LEADER,
ADMIRAL KARL DOENITZ.

NOTHING WILL CHANGE. ALL CITIZENS WILL
REPORT TO THEIR PLACES OF WORK AS USUAL.
FAILURE TO ATTEND IS PUNISHABLE BY DEATH.

THE FUEHRER, ADMIRAL KARL DOENITZ.

Kees shook his head in dismay. "I was afraid this would happen. It seems our joyful little celebration was a bit early. We had better be careful." He pushed off again and pedaled toward home. They were getting close now.

They turned onto the Deiman Straat, where the van Rijn's house sat next door to the Groenendijk warehouse, and pedaled up the street. They smiled as their home could be seen far ahead.

"There it is!" Cornelius cried out, and Johanna hugged him. As they got closer their smiles faded away. The house looked all wrong. As they rolled to a stop in front, they saw why.

The house at Number 396 had been completely ransacked.

There were no windows left, and the front door was gone, leaving their home wide open to the world. In stunned silence, they entered the front hallway. The house was empty, nothing at all was left. No kitchen, no bathroom, even the faucets had been taken. No lamps were left, not even the light switches. The vandals, perhaps the NSB, had ripped every single thing out of the house. It was an empty shell.

"Nothing," Kees said, darkly. "There is nothing."

Up until then, Johanna had managed to keep her emotions in check. They had been through so much, and she'd had to be strong. But now, after all that they'd suffered, to have her home taken away at the end. It all came flooding out of her, "How can our own people be so cruel?" She began to cry, "We can't live in our house anymore. Kees, what will we do now?"

Cornelius began crying too, then through his sobs he yelled, "My garden! What's happened to my plants and flowers?" He dashed through the house and stepped through the opening that had been their back door. Kees and Johanna followed.

At the top of his voice, Cornelius cried out in joy, "My plants are still there! My marigolds are blooming, and the potatoes have come up! Even the strawberries are blooming!"

He bent over and plucked a large, ripe strawberry from one of his plants. It was bright red and juicy. "They left the best for you, Mom. Don't cry," Cornelius said, as he gave it to his mother. "We'll fix it. We'll fix it all. My plants are still here and growing. We'll just take care of the house and grow it back, too."

Johanna laughed through her tears at her son's heady optimism, and she resolved at that moment to let nothing defeat her. "God has blessed us, and kept us from entering the gates of hell. There is nothing left to do, but trust Him," she said. She knelt down beside Cornelius and gave him a kiss. "Son, you are absolutely right. We'll fix everything, won't we, dad?"

"It will be a big job," Kees said from behind her, "but that's exactly what we'll do."

Turning to face Kees, Johanna saw that he was already planning his next step. "Okay, Mr. Resistance leader," she said, "what are we doing next?"

"Let's go see Frans. He can help." Kees stopped suddenly, as he realized his mistake. They had lost their friend Frans in the camp at Bergen-Belsen. "Oh, my God, how could I forget?"

Johanna said, "Let's go see Anna."

CHAPTER FORTY-NINE

Bringing Bad News

Together, the van Rijn family walked to the house one street over, on the Drebbel Straat. Anna saw them coming and ran to open the door. "What a wonderful surprise," she called out happily, "How did you get out of jail?" She hugged each one of them in turn, welcoming them into her home.

"Did they let you go when Hitler died? Where is Frans? Did they let him out, too?" She looked at Kees, then at Johanna, waiting for her answer. Then, their somber expressions registered in her mind, and her demeanor changed quickly. "Tell me, please, where is my husband? Tell me what has happened, please."

"Anna, you must sit down," Kees said, "because I have a long and sad story to tell."

They could see the tears coming to Anna's eyes. "Please don't tell me that Frans . . ."

Kees put his arm around her, and Johanna took up her hands. "Anna, we're sorry, but Frans is not with us. The last time that we saw him was in the concentration camp at Bergen-Belsen."

"Is there any hope that he will come home from there too?" she interrupted.

Kees didn't answer, but instead waved her to the sofa. He sat alongside her, and Johanna sat at her other side. Cornelius took a soft chair across the room and watched them quietly.

Kees told her of the the many Jews that they were trying to hide, and of their arrest. He told her about the torture they had suffered, and Anna sobbed at the news. Then, he explained how clever Frans had been, fooling the Nazis with a list of empty hiding places. Hope began to show again on Anna's face.

"On the fifth day," Kees said, "Johanna and Cornelius came to my cell. She cleaned me up of blood, and brought fresh clothes. When she finished, they brought a truck to take us all home."

Anna brightened a little at the thought.

"But that truck took us to the train instead. The train to the camps," Kees continued. As she listened, Anna's head dipped, afraid of what might come next.

"The trip on that train," Kees said darkly, "I'll spare you the awful details, but it lasted four days and nights. Hundreds of us crushed into that car without food, drink, or a toilet. When we finally arrived, it was midnight. We were all soiled and exhausted, more than thirty people came out dead."

Anna began to cry softly then. Johanna put an arm around her shoulders and held her tightly. Her other hand, she put in Anna's lap, and Anna clutched it tightly.

"After four days on our feet, we could no longer walk," Kees said, "so we crawled into a barracks that was already full of people. And still, no water or food.

"The next morning, the sound of gunfire woke us up. Then, all hell broke loose, as the armies of heaven crashed through the walls. Tanks and trucks and thousands of soldiers charged into the camp to capture the Nazis."

In her heart, Anna knew what was coming, but she couldn't help it as her hopes rose a little once again.

"The British gave us food, and drink, and new clothes to wear. Then, they began to register us. An officer asked for my name, so I gave it—and he knew who I was before I'd even finished answering him!

Through her tears, Anna wrinkled her brow in puzzlement. "A British soldier already knew you?" she asked.

"He had been my radio contact in London," Kees nodded. "He arranged for a truck to bring us back to Holland right away. I told the officer that my partner, Frans, was there with us; but we had lost him. I asked if he would find him and send him home with us to Holland," Kees paused and looked at Anna.

She nodded for him to go on. "Tell me," she said.

"The officer sent two soldiers to look for Frans. They found him, but . . . 'I am so sorry' they said, 'he has passed away.'"

Anna turned very pale and passed out.

Kees and Johanna laid her out carefully on the sofa. Johanna went to the kitchen and came back with a damp cloth, which she used to gently wipe away Anna's tears and cool off her forehead. Slowly, Anna came back around.

Once she was alert again, Anna said, "I had a dream. I saw Frans in heaven. He told me he was well, and that I should be happy that God had saved him from a great deal of pain."

"That's a wonderful gift you've been given," Johanna said, "to see Frans once more, and know that he is well."

"Thank you," Anna said. "He looked good. And thank you for taking care of me. It was just too much to take in at once."

"I know. I will always be here to help," Johanna said. "And I wonder if you might be able to help us?"

"Why, what do you need?" Anna asked, in sudden concern for her friend.

"We have nowhere to go. Our house has been completely ransacked. There is nothing left, but an empty shell," Johanna sighed. "Everything has been taken: the doors, the windows, the whole kitchen, even the lamps and the light switches are gone. We can't possibly live in it."

"Well then you'll just have to stay here with me," Anna said. "I was trying to figure out how to ask you anyway. I could use your company."

"Really?" Johanna said, "That would be wonderful."

"I would love it if you'd stay with me until your house is a real home again," Anna smiled wistfully. "And it would be better not to be alone."

"Thank you, so very much," Johanna said, as they hugged each other and cried together a little bit more, both from sadness mixed with joy.

ONCE THINGS had quieted down again, Kees returned to his skeletal house to retrieve the box-bicycle he'd left there. There he saw, to his great surprise, that his front door had been reinstalled! He couldn't imagine how it had been done while they were gone. He looked around the neighborhood to see if anyone was about, and his neighbor came out of his house.

"Kees, you're back! What a nice surprise to see you at home once again!"

"Yes, it's nice to be home," Kees said, ". . . or what's left of it anyway."

"I am sorry about your house. The NSB came . . . with guns."

"Well, it's just a house," Kees said. "Nothing worth getting killed over."

"The NSB-ers were stealing everything," Kees' neighbor said. "When they left with a load, I came over and removed the door, before they came back for more. They never even noticed.

"I hoped that you might come back one day, and you would need it to start again."

"It will help," Kees said, "thank you."

"I can help, too," his neighbor replied.

"It's good to be home again," Kees said, smiling as he shook the man's hand. "You shouldn't have risked it, but I really do appreciate it."

"Our recovery has begun," Kees announced when he returned to Anna's house. "Our neighbor saved our front door for us, and he reinstalled it already this morning. We can now start making our house habitable again."

"And so it begins," Johanna smiled.

"More good news," he added. "I checked our savings account, and it's all still there."

"The banks are already open again?" Johanna asked.

"No, not that savings account," Kees grinned. "The one in the backyard, buried under the bench. It was all there.

"I'm so glad we took the time to do that. Otherwise it woud all be in the hands of the NSB."

CHAPTER FIFTY

Countdown to Liberation

I t was May 1, 1945, and all day long there were thousands of Allied bombers and cargo planes in the skies over Holland. This time, they came in low, but no bombs tumbled from the bomb bay doors. Instead it was large cargo canisters.

The end of the war was days away, and the Netherlands were at a standstill. Trade had come to a halt, and food shipments stopped completely. This only compounded the famine that most of Holland was already suffering. The powerful German armies had yet to surrender or leave, while the Allied armies waited in the southern end of the country. A house-to-house battle to liberate the rest of the Netherlands would be devastating. Instead it was decided that all sides would wait for the upcoming surrender to take place.

Meanwhile, the Dutch people starved. Allied officers negotiated with *Reichskommissar* Seyss-Inquart for a partial cease-fire which would allow humanitarian airdrops to take place. Eventually, even truck convoys would be allowed behind enemy lines.

The airdrops took place everywhere, dropping all manner of dry goods and tinned foods. Chocolate, cigarettes, crackers, pancake mix, and cans of anchovies, Spam, and powdered milk could be found inside the big cargo canisters. The goods were distributed to the citizens, but the process was chaotic at best.

With weapons in hand, the remaining German soldiers still claimed first choice. They had no qualms about benefitting from Allied largesse. They were hungry, too.

By May 2, those citizens who still had radios hidden away came onto the streets each day to spread their news messages. According to Radio Orange, the Dutch radio broadcast made through the BBC, Hitler was most definitely dead.

A few stores begin to sell food again, but the food was scarce and it sold at exorbitant prices. A loaf of bread was seventy guilders (about $23), a pound of butter was one hundred and thirty guilders ($43), a pound of sugar was eighty-five guilders ($28) and a pound of bacon was two hundred guilders ($67). *(At the time, the exchange rate was about three guilders to the dollar.)*

By May 3, the news was out. Berlin had fallen to the Soviets, and the German armies there had all surrendered. The Germans were pushed from Finland. Denmark was liberated, and nearly a million German soldiers had surrendered to the Allies in Italy and Austria. The war must be over by now, the people thought, but where is the peace? Holland remained in a state of war, and armed Nazi soldiers continued to patrol the streets. The citizens wondered, *when will our country truly be free?*

On May 4, Queen Wilhelmina and Princess Juliana returned to the Netherlands. They flew in from England, to an airport in the south of the province of Brabant. They were home to stay.

Rumors circulated that in two days the people could hang out their flags, because on that day the Canadian armies would finally enter the cities.

The Dutch national anthem, *Het Wilhelmus*, played loudly through an illegal radio from a window in The Hague. People ran through the streets in sudden excitement toward the house. The crowd gathered below the window and defiantly sang along with the radio.

Everyone was wearing orange, the color was symbolic of the Dutch royal family. The crowd danced and sang, and they cheered wildly, "At last, it's over! We are liberated! Liberated!" *Surely the war must be over by now*, they thought.

Some of German soldiers were intoxicated—they had been drinking both in celebration and in despair—and they joined in on the revelry. As the crowds grew in size, the soldiers could be seen dancing and singing drunkenly with the Dutch crowds.

At midnight, suddenly a fusillade of gunfire could be heard. In seconds, the streets were cleared of people, as everyone ran to find cover. But nothing would stifle the joy of liberation. A few drunken Nazis had simply grown weary of the celebration and opened fire to silence the revelers. A group of men overpowered and disarmed the disorderly troopers. The Germans were tied up with rope, laid in the gutter, and left to sober up.

On May 5, the official capitulation of the Nazi forces in the Netherlands was announced. The occupation wass over. Dutch flags were out everywhere, hanging from windows and fluttering in the breeze. And yet, heavily-armed Nazi soldiers continued to walk around as if they owned the place. Many of the officers wisely stayed holed up in their offices and seized villas. The atmosphere was becoming tense and uncertain.

Members of the BS *(Binnenlandse Strijdkrachten)*, or Dutch National Guard, began to show up on the streets. They carried weapons for the first time in five years.

Three of guardsmen paid a visit to the mayor of the city. A German sentry stood guard in front of the mayor's home. He politely allowed these Dutch soldiers to enter the house, when suddenly, a large group of Nazi soldiers charged into the otherwise calm scene. They lowered their submachine guns menacingly at the Dutch soldiers.

A Nazi officer in charge of the detail shouted, *"Nicht schiesen, nur entwaffenen."* (Don't shoot, just take their guns.) The three guardsmen raised their hands and they were taken away at gunpoint, as if they were a gang of criminals. *"So weit ist es noch nicht"* (That time has not arrived yet.)

That evening the Queen gave a short speech during a special radio broadcast. Those who still had radios pointed them out to the streets so that everyone could hear. Her message contained the urgent warning, "Please, do not engage in any arguments with the remaining German soldiers. Try to understand that they are normal human beings who will want to return to their families, too.

"The soldiers who have mistreated our citizens will be found and punished by a court of law in due time. We urge you to celebrate our liberation in peace. Do not take the law in your own hands in regards to known members of the NSB. They too, will be judged in time, according to the laws of our great country.

"May God be with you and your families. We are free again, liberated from the Nazi oppression."

On May 6, early in the morning, the entire population of the country turned out. They gathered in the streets, waving flags or wearing orange flowers. Dutch flags, banners, and handmade signs were displayed everywhere. The queen's radio broadcast inspired the public to demonstrate their happiness, but to do so peacefully. There would be no mobs , no more violence, no acts of vengeance. The people were free again, and the queen was back, so life would return to normal.

As the festivities continued, Cornelius saw his opportunity. He went into the backyard, picked all of his orange marigolds, and sold them on the street for a guilder apiece. Once he had picked and sold the last flower, he counted up his money. "That's three-hundred-and-seventy-one guilders!" He asked his father, "Can we buy mom a new kitchen for that?"

"It will be a big help!" Kees said, "I can add some money, too. We'll get a nice kitchen as soon as the stores have something back in stock again."

Kees had dug up their pre-war "savings account" from beneath the bench in the backyard. The silver two-and-a-half guilder coins amounted to thousands of guilders. Restoring their home had become Kees' primary concern.

CHAPTER FIFTY-ONE

Restoring the House

The war was over, and the Nazis had finally left Holland and gone back to where they belonged. It was just as well, they had a shattered country to rebuild at home . . . or, at least half of one. The eastern half of Germany would remain firmly in control of the communists for the next 44 years, so great was the Soviet fear that the Germans might rise again.

The NSB-ers in Holland had been rounded up. Many had escaped to Germany. Others tried to go into hiding, but it was no use. By their own despicable behavior, they had made themselves too well known and thoroughly reviled. All were facing court cases, and many received jail sentences of up to twenty-five years. Some of the worst would suffer the death penalty.

The factories reopened and resumed production, but it was slow going at first. Until trade was fully resumed, raw materials remained scarce; and store shelves were often too empty.

Kees found some plywood available from one storekeeper. It was enough to board up their empty windows and the back door. Kees had to pay the merchant far too much; but if he didn't, then soon there would be nothing left to do the job.

"Cornelius, we need a saw and some nails," Kees said, "so we can secure our house again. Why don't we go and get some?"

At the hardware store, the owner was busy checking his small inventory. He had a few items available, but they were mostly things that nobody needed. The basic necessities were in short supply everywhere.

"Can we get a pound of nails," Kees asked the shopkeeper.

The man shook his head. "I'm sorry, but we have none to give you. The factory can't get any metal to make their nails yet. They told me it would be two months before they could supply us with any more."

When Cornelius heard that, he thought of all the nails that stuck out from the boards in the bombed-out houses he used to play in. He planned to pull them all out, one by one. In the soil of his garden he had found an old rusty claw-hammer. It had no handle, but with some patience Cornelius managed to create one, using an old piece of a broken broomstick. After hours of carving and tinkering he was able to create a useful hammer.

Pulling the nails out wasn't too hard. Unfortunately, they all came out bent or crooked. With a good deal of patient tapping, he was able to straighten out the nails. Cornelius returned home one evening with a dozen useful nails in his little hand. He handed them to his father, and said, "I'm in the nail business now. Here are a dozen nails to get you started. If you want more, they will be ten cents apiece *(about 3¢ US)*."

"Like everything else, the cost seems to have gone up," Kees said, as he winked at his entrepreneurial little boy.

"These are handmade, dad," Cornelius said earnestly. "I have to find them by hand, pull them by hand, and straighten them by hand."

"Well, they are a bargain then!" Kees said with a smile.

"You have to pay for quality, Kees," Johanna quipped.

From that day on, Cornelius went to the ruins every day and pulled as many nails as he could find. He even sold them to the hardware store for ten cents each.

It took the van Rijns six months of hard work before they were able to move into their home once more. It was several years before the country was operating as normal again. By then, Kees had resumed his job as a corporate lawyer.

Cornelius' older siblings, two brothers and a sister, returned home from the farms in northern Holland, where they had spent the war. That September, Cornelius went to school for the first time in his life.

Many everyday needs, like new clothes and shoes, were still in short supply in Holland, so Cornelius walked to school wearing his wooden shoes. His friends made fun of him for the clip-clop noise he made while walking the streets.

Sometimes, Cornelius remembered the clip-clop noise that the train had made on the tracks, on the trip to Bergen-Belsen.

This was much better.

Miracles Still Happen

It was 2014, sixty-nine years after the end of the war, and Cornelius was driving through the Holland countryside. He accidently drove right past his destination, the old farmhouse where the Brandwijk family used to live. He was seventy-four years old now, Cornelius consoled himself. It was okay if he missed a tiny detail now and then, as long as he got to where he needed to go in the end.

The stable and the great haystack were gone now. The beautiful fields and meadows had filled up with new housing developments and little rows of shops. The land looked prosperous. It was almost hard to imagine that war had really happened here.

Cornelius reflected on the time he had spent with his dear friend, Marie, with whom he had once been very much in love. He wondered, was she still alive? He hadn't seen her since the end of the war. It was all so long ago.

Rolling to a stop at the former farmhouse, Cornelius pulled himself out of the car and climbed the front steps to the porch. He rang the doorbell and heard the old, familiar sound. A gentleman of about sixty-some years of age opened the door.

"There used to be a family that lived here, by the name of Brandwijk," Cornelius said. "Are they still around?"

The gentleman shook his head, "Mr. and Mrs. Brandwijk were my grandparents. They both passed away back in 1989."

"They had a daughter by the name of Marie. Your mother, I presume?" Cornelius asked hopefully, "Can you tell me what's happened to her?"

"Yes, you're right. Marie is my mother. She is alive and well, and living in a retirement home in the province of Groningen. But may I ask, who are you?"

"I was a childhood friend of hers," Cornelius replied.

"Would you like to go and see her?" the gentleman asked. Cornelius heart skipped a beat. "I can give you the address."

It was 110 kilometers away. Less than two hours later, Cornelius walked into the main hall of the home. Dozens of elderly people relaxed at the tables, playing games and chatting together. Cornelius just stood there, wondering how he would find her.

Across the room, one of the ladies looked in his direction, and called out, "Cornelius! Is that you?" Tears of joy filled his eyes. There was Marie, and even after so many years, he still recognized her familiar, smiling, lovely face.

Marie and Cornelius spent the rest of the day together, catching up on a lifetime's worth of stories. They took turns telling them to each other, and they laughed long into the night.

It was a miracle to see that they could still share a flame which had been kindled some seventy years ago.

THE END OF PART THREE

D irk van Leenen was born in 1940, just as the Second World War began for the Netherlands. For many years, he used to tell stories about his experiences as a child during the war years in Holland.

Dirk's mother was Jewish, so his parents were active in the Dutch Resistance. They risked their lives to hide Jewish familes from the Germans and then shepherd them to safety. It is out of their stories and anecdotes, and Dirk's own memories, that these stories are brought to life again.

Dirk's children and grandchildren listened to his stories with rapt attention, and constantly urged him to write a book about those difficult times. This is Dirk's third book. He has also spoken with many Holocaust survivors and gathered stories which have never been told.

His interest in English literature began when he studied English at the University of Leiden. He worled for a number of years in Holland as an English teacher. Dirk also has several degrees in horticultre and floral design, and has spent much of his life working with flowers.

Dirk is happily married to Cynthia June van Leenen, with whom he has seven children and seventeen grandchildren. They live quietly in Arizona, where they enjoy time with their grandchildren, and Dirk continues to write his stories.